VOL **1** A-AQU
1–86

FUNK & WAGNALLS **new**

ENCYCLOPEDIA
OF SCIENCE

FUNK & WAGNALLS, INC.

HOW TO USE FUNK & WAGNALLS NEW ENCYCLOPEDIA OF SCIENCE

Volumes 1 through 21 have information printed on the front covers, spine, and title pages that make it easy to find the articles you want to read.

- Volume numbers are printed in all three places in Volumes 1 through 21.
- Letter breaks — $\frac{COL}{DIA}$ — are printed in all three places in Volumes 1 through 21. The letters above the line are the first three letters of the first article title in the volume. The letters below the line are the first three letters of the last article title in the volume.
- Page breaks — $\frac{351}{438}$ — are printed on the spines and title pages of Volumes 1 through 21. They provide the page numbers of the first and last text pages in the volume.

Articles are arranged alphabetically by title in Volumes 1 through 21. Most titles are printed in **BOLD-FACE CAPITAL** letters. Some titles are printed in even larger letters.

- Some titles are not article titles, but refer you to the actual article title. Within articles you will find *See* or *See also* other article names for further information. All of these references to other articles are called cross-references.
- Most article titles are followed by a phonetic pronunciation. Use the Pronunciation Guide on page vi of Volume 1 to learn the correct pronunciation of the article title.
- At the end of most articles are two sets of initials. The first set identifies the person who wrote the article. The second set identifies the special consultant who checked the article for accuracy. All of these people are listed by their initials and full names and position on pages v and vi of Volume 1.
- ◥ This symbol at the end of an article indicates that there is a project based on the subject of the article in the Projects, Bibliography & Index volume. The project is found under its article title, and all of the project article titles are arranged alphabetically on pages 1 through 64 of the Projects, Bibliography & Index volume.

The Projects, Bibliography & Index Volume contains three sections. Each is an essential part of the encyclopedia.

- Projects based on articles in the encyclopedia are found in the first section. Each is both entertaining and educational. Each is designed for use by a student and for parental participation if desired.
- Bibliography reading lists in the second section list books under general scientific categories that are also titles of major articles. Each book listed is marked with either a YA (Young Adult) or J (Juvenile) reading level indicator. YA generally applies to readers at the junior high level or higher. J applies to readers at grade levels below junior high school.
- Index entries for all article titles plus many subjects that are not article titles are found in the third section. Instructions on using the Index are found at the start of the Index section in the Projects, Bibliography & Index volume.

PRONUNCIATION GUIDE

These symbols have the same sound as the
darker letters in the sample words.

ə	balloon, ago	i	rip, ill	t	to, stand
ər	learn, further	ī	side, sky	th	thin, death
a	map, have	j	join, germ	<u>th</u>	then, this
ā	day, made	k	king, ask	ü	pool, lose
ä	father, car	l	let, cool	u̇	put, book
au̇	now, loud	m	man, same	v	view, give
b	ball, rib	n	no, turn	w	wood, glowing
ch	choose, nature	ō	cone, know	y	yes, year
d	did, add	ȯ	all, saw	z	zero, raise
e	bell, get	ȯi	boy, boil	zh	leisure, vision
ē	sweet, easy	p	part, scrap		
f	fan, soft	r	root, tire	′	strong accent
g	good, big	s	so, press	′	weak accent
h	hurt, ahead	sh	shoot, machine		

A

AARDVARK (ärd' värk) The aardvark is an African mammal of the family Orycteropodidae. It is found from Ethiopia to South Africa. Aardvark means ''earth pig'' in the Afrikaans language. The aardvark is about the size of a pig. It has a long snout. Its tongue can be extended 45 cm [18 in]. Aardvarks range in color from dull brownish gray to sandy yellow.

Aardvarks are nocturnal, which means they are active at night. They use their sharp claws to dig into ant and termite hills. With their long tongues, they scoop up and eat the insects.   S.R.G./J.J.M.

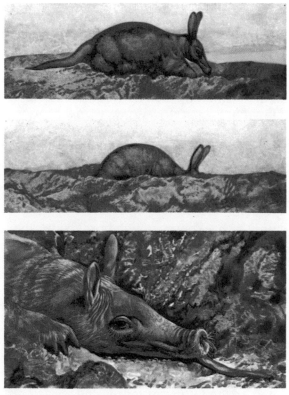

The aardvark can dig itself into the earth in a few minutes. Its claws are well suited for this task. Its tongue is especially suited for getting food. The bottom picture shows how this animal uses its tongue to capture termites and ants.

The aardwolf is related to the hyenas. Unlike the hyenas, the aardwolf has weak teeth and jaws. It feeds on small animals, including termites. Aardwolves do their hunting at night.

AARDWOLF (ärd' wúlf) The aardwolf is an African mammal which belongs to the hyena family Hyaenidae. This uncommon animal is found from South Africa to Angola.

Although it resembles a hyena, the aardwolf is much smaller. It grows to only 75 cm [30 in]. The fur of the aardwolf is grayish yellow with black markings. Aardwolves spend the days in their underground holes. They come out at night to hunt small animals and termites, their major source of food.

S.R.G./J.J.M.

ABACUS (ab' ə kəs) An abacus is a device once widely used for counting. The Chinese began using the abacus about 5,000 years ago. An abacus has beads that are moved up and down on wires that are strung in a frame. For example, the Russian abacus has ten wires with ten beads strung on each. The beads on the wire farthest to the right have the value of units, or ones. Those on the next wire contain the value of tens. Those on the next contain the value of hundreds, and so on. Every time all of the beads have been used on one wire, one bead is moved up on the next wire. Then, the beads on the completed wire are moved back.

The Chinese abacus is similar. However, it uses only seven beads on each wire. Two of the beads are separated from the others by a

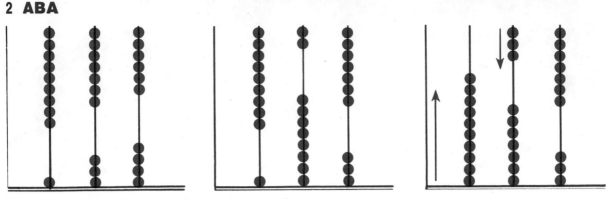

The abacus is a counting frame that was once used in schools for teaching arithmetic. Each bead represents a number. By moving the beads in certain ways, the operator of the abacus can quickly add, subtract, multiply, or divide numbers. The answer depends on how many rows of beads are used.

bar. The beads below the bar on the right hand wire have a value of one unit each. The beads above have a value of five units each. The Japanese abacus also uses a bar, with one bead above the bar and four below.

Once the abacus is mastered, a person can add, subtract, multiply, and divide quickly by moving the beads about. *See also* COMPUTER.

J.J.A./S.P.A.

The abalone (left) is a single-shelled mollusk. It is a distant relative of the snails. A main feature of the abalone is the row of holes in its shell.

ABALONE (ab′ ə lō′ nē) The abalone is a large marine mollusk belonging to the class Gastropoda. It is found off the coasts of California, Australia, and South Africa. The abalone has one shell, which is shaped like a dish. It covers the top of the animal. The abalone grows up to 30 cm [1 ft] long. There is a row of holes along one edge of the shell through which water passes. The gills of the abalone enable it to breathe the way fish breathe. The inside of the shell is a beautiful white mineral which is called mother-of-pearl. Mother-of-pearl is used in jewelry. The large, muscular foot is called abalone steak when it is eaten by humans. S.R.G./C.S.H.

ABDOMEN (ab′ də mən) The abdomen is a section of the body of an animal. In humans it is often called the belly. On humans, the abdomen begins at the bottom of the chest and ends at the hips. The abdomen contains many important organs such as the stomach, the intestines, the kidneys, and the liver. These organs are kept in place by strong muscles, and some are protected by the bones of the spine, or backbone, which borders the abdomen. The diaphragm separates the abdomen from the chest, where the lungs and heart are. (*See* ANATOMY.)

In insects, the abdomen is the last body segment. No legs are found on this segment. (*See* INSECT.) S.R.G./J.J.F.

ABERRATION (ab′ ə rā′ shən) Aberration refers to the failure of lenses and curved mirrors to form sharp images. The light rays from an object are not brought to a sharp focus. This is not because the lens is not well made.

It is because there are no "perfect" lens or mirror surfaces that will always produce sharp images. There are several kinds of aberration: chromatic aberration, spherical aberration, coma, distortion, astigmatism, and field curvature.

Chromatic aberration occurs because the lens bends blue light more than red light. White light is made up of all the pure colors, so the lens forms images that are bordered by colored fringes or rings. An achromatic lens is a combination of two lenses made of different kinds of glass. It helps to reduce the color fringing. Achromatic lenses are used in telescopes and in most cameras.

Spherical aberration results from a lens (or a dish-shaped mirror) forming images that are slightly fuzzy. In other words, light rays from an object that pass through the lens will not all meet in a sharp image. The curvature of the mirror or lens surfaces can be slightly reshaped to reduce spherical aberration. Using only the central part of the lens or mirror also helps. However, this reduces the brightness of the image.

Coma is the aberration that causes the image of a point to be comet or pear-shaped. This happens when rays of light from the point form overlapping images.

A lens afflicted with distortion shows straight lines as slightly curved. The image of an object will be out of proportion.

The aberration of astigmatism gives fuzzy images in which a point might appear as a vertical or a horizontal line, in front or in back of the best obtainable image. A related aberration is called curvature of field. For instance, the image of an extensive object like a landscape does not lie in a flat plane, but rather on a curved surface. The effect in a camera, where the film is flat, is that the entire image cannot be in focus. If objects near the center of the film are sharp, those around the edges will be fuzzy.

All the aberrations can be reduced by replacing single lenses with special combinations of lenses. A high-quality camera lens, for example, may consist of as many as six or eight component lenses.   W.R.P./S.S.B.

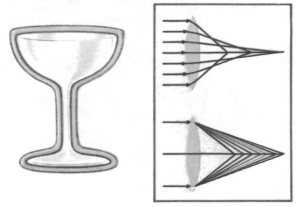

The colored sparkle of a wine glass is due to chromatic aberration. The diagram at the right shows two kinds of aberration seen when light passes through a lens. The upper lens shows spherical aberration, in which light focuses differently in different parts of the lens. The lower lens shows chromatic aberration.

ABORTION (ə bôr′ shən) An abortion is the death of an unborn child, or fetus, during the first 19 weeks of pregnancy. The mother's body will usually reject the dead fetus, causing it to leave her body. At other times, a doctor must remove the dead fetus. The death may be caused by many things. The fetus may develop incorrectly, or the mother may become ill or injured. The death of a fetus is also called a miscarriage.

Sometimes the fetus is not healthy. Sometimes the mother's health is in danger. In such cases, doctors cause the abortion of the fetus. It used to be illegal for doctors to perform an abortion unless the mother's life was in danger. Today, in many areas of the United States, doctors are allowed to perform abortions because the mother doesn't wish to have a baby, even if she is healthy. *See also* EMBRYO.   S.R.G./J.J.F.

ABRASIVE (ə brā′ siv) An abrasive is a material used to grind, wear down, scrape, or polish other materials. The two main forms of abrasives are paper and grinding wheels.

An extreme kind of abrasion is shown by the action of this grinding wheel on a block of metal.

Abrasive paper is made by coating paper with a glue and adding the abrasive substance. Sandpaper, emery paper, and Carborundum paper are made in this way. To make a grinding wheel, abrasive material such as quartz is mixed with clay and water. This mixture is then pressed into the desired size and shape and fired in a furnace. The heat makes a strong bond among the materials.

A grit number is used to describe the fineness or coarseness of the particles used in an abrasive material. Abrasives with a grit number of 60 are much finer than abrasives with a grit number of 30.

The hardness of an abrasive is important. An abrasive must be harder than the material it is meant to grind or polish. The hardness of minerals is measured according to a scale known as Mohs scale. (*See* HARDNESS.)

Mohs scale ranges from 1 to 10. The higher the number, the harder the material. Talc, a soft mineral used in face powder, has a value of 1. Diamond, the hardest mineral on Mohs scale, has a value of 10.

The most widely used abrasives are fused aluminum oxide (Al_2O_3) and silicon carbide (SiC). Aluminum oxide is known as alumina. It is used to grind and polish metals like steel, wrought iron, and hard bronze. Silicon carbide is better known as Carborundum. It is made by fusing sand and coke in an electric furnace. Carborundum is used to grind and polish brass, copper, aluminum, stone, glass, and ceramics.

Varieties of quartz are also important abrasives. Pumice is a volcanic rock. When ground to a fine powder, it is used in scouring powders and soaps. Diatomite is the chalky remains of tiny organisms. (*See* ALGAE.) It is used in metal polishes. Crystalline iron oxide is used to polish jewelry and glass. It is known as jeweler's rouge because of its reddish color.

Synthetic diamonds and diamonds not suitable for gemstones are used as abrasives. They provide a hard edge in the drill bits used in drilling through rock for oil. Tungsten carbide (WC) is used in the machine tool industry for the drilling, cutting, and polishing of metals. The carbides, nitrides, and borides of tantalum, vanadium, and zirconium are similar in hardness to tungsten carbide and are used for the same purposes. Another important abrasive is boron carbide (B_4C). It is valuable because it is almost as hard as diamond. J.J.A./R.H.

ABSOLUTE ZERO (ab′ sə lüt′ zē′ rō) Absolute zero, the complete absence of heat, is a concept derived from the third law of thermodynamics, according to which the lowest temperature possible is $-273.16°C$ [$-459.69°F$]. These numbers are based on the theory that the volume of a gas gets smaller as its temperature is lowered. (*See* CHARLES' LAW.) In this theory, the volume of a gas would disappear if its temperature were lowered to $-273.16°C$, or absolute zero. The gas molecules would be completely at rest, and the substance would possess no heat at all. In actual practice, however, all gases change to liquids and/or solids before their temperature reaches absolute zero.

Scientists have never been able to reach absolute zero in laboratory experiments. The lowest recorded temperature was achieved by magnetizing copper nuclei at a low temperature. When the magnet was turned off, the copper nuclei became demagnetized and cooled to within millionths of a degree above absolute zero.

Materials cooled to temperatures near absolute zero react strangely. Oxygen freezes to a bluish white solid; a rubber ball becomes so brittle that it shatters instead of bouncing. Mercury, normally liquid, looks and acts like hard silver. Hydrogen becomes a liquid and begins creeping up the sides of its container. Natural gas is shipped around the world in special containers after being cooled and liquified in this way.

The temperature at which the volume of a gas would disappear is given the value of zero on the Kelvin scale. The Kelvin scale is used for scientific measurements. Absolute zero on the Kelvin scale is expressed as zero Kelvin (0 K). The degree sign (°) is not used in the Kelvin scale. *See also* CRYOGENICS; KELVIN SCALE; LORD KELVIN. W.R.P./R.W.L.

ABSORPTION AND ADSORPTION Absorption (əb sȯrp′ shən) and adsorption (ad sȯrp′ shən) are two different ways for a substance to take up another substance. In absorption, the second substance becomes spread throughout the first substance. In adsorption, the second substance is spread only on the surface of the first substance.

Substances can also absorb various forms of energy, such as heat, light, and sound. When energy is absorbed by an object, the energy usually changes form. People are warmed when they absorb the sun's rays. All colored objects have a certain color because they reflect that color. They absorb all the others. For example, a blue object absorbs nearly all the light striking its surface except blue light, which is reflected. Sunlight and other white light are a mixture of all colors. A black object absorbs all of the light falling on it. Sound is absorbed by heavy curtains and soundproofing materials. These materials are often found in recording studios, concert halls, and auditoriums. The materials absorb internally produced sounds and prevent them from producing echoes and reverberations.

Liquids absorb gases and solids by dissolving them. The sea absorbs oxygen from the air and from plant life in the water. The absorption of gases is important in industry. Many gases are purified by passing them up a tower containing streams of falling liq-

ABSORPTION AND ADSORPTION

White light is composed of many colors. These colors can be separated by a prism as shown in this picture. When we see an object as colored, this means that only that color is being reflected. When we see blue, for example, only blue light is being reflected. All other colors are being absorbed.
Left: pigment in our skin absorbs ultraviolet radiation from the sun. In doing so, it darkens, and we become suntanned.

ammonia
gas

ammonia
solution

water
containing
red litmus

The "ammonia fountain" at left shows chemical absorption. Acid water is drawn up through ammonia gas and is changed to an alkaline solution. Litmus dye shows the changing of acid (red) to alkaline (blue). Right: The coloring matter of brown sugar is chemically adsorbed by charcoal. When a solution of brown sugar is filtered through charcoal, it loses its brown color. The brown pigments remain on the charcoal filter. The colorless liquid is a sugar solution. Crystals of white sugar are recovered from this solution.

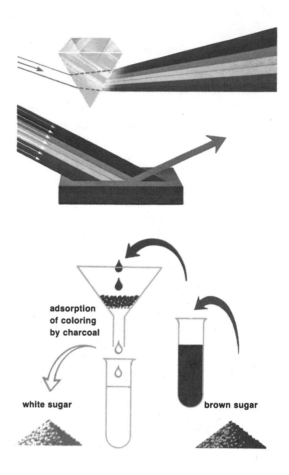

adsorption
of coloring
by charcoal

white sugar

brown sugar

uid. The liquid absorbs the impurities in the gases. The towers are called absorption towers or scrubbers.

Blood absorbs oxygen from the air in the lungs and carries it to the body tissues. This keeps us alive.

When a porous solid, such as a sponge or dry earth, absorbs a liquid, what actually happens is that the countless interior surfaces of the tiny pore spaces in the solid adsorb the liquid. Solids adsorb liquids by surface attraction.

Solids also adsorb gases. Powerful solid adsorbents, like charcoal, can adsorb up to ninety times their volume of a gas. Charcoal is used in gas masks to remove large amounts of poisonous or impure gases from the air that the person wearing the mask breathes. Char-

coal is also used to remove odors and coloring matter from solids and liquids. W.R.P./A.D.

ACCELERATION (ik sel′ ə rā′ shən) Acceleration is the rate at which the velocity of something changes. An airplane roaring down the runway during takeoff is accelerating rapidly. In a drag race, the drivers try to reach the highest possible velocity after a short distance. To do this, they have to accelerate as much as possible.

Acceleration is always caused by a force. In a car or plane, the force is produced by the engine. The amount of acceleration for a body of a certain mass is directly related to the force. If the force is doubled, the acceleration is also doubled. But if the body is twice as heavy, the same force accelerates it only half as much. This is why a truck needs a more powerful engine than a small car.

A force can also slow an object down. It does this when it acts in the opposite direction to the motion. This is sometimes called deceleration.

A force can also act at an angle to the object. This changes the direction in which it is going. This is still an acceleration because the velocity has changed. Velocity is not the same as speed. The speed of a body is its rate of travel in any direction. Velocity is a speed in a particular direction, so if either the speed or the direction changes, then the velocity also changes. When an object moves in a circle, its speed can stay the same but its direction is continually changing. Therefore, its velocity is continually changing. For example, the velocity of a spacecraft in orbit is always changing, even when its speed stays the same. The force that causes the velocity to change is the force of gravity. *See also* DYNAMICS.

M.E./J.T.

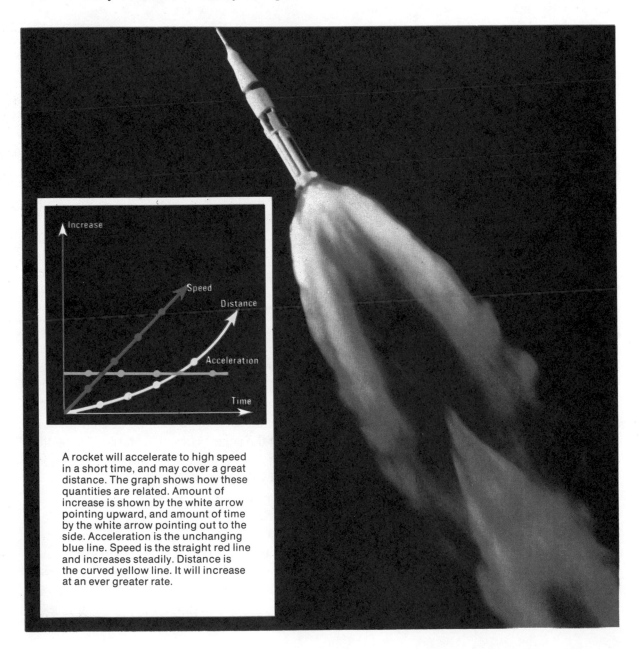

A rocket will accelerate to high speed in a short time, and may cover a great distance. The graph shows how these quantities are related. Amount of increase is shown by the white arrow pointing upward, and amount of time by the white arrow pointing out to the side. Acceleration is the unchanging blue line. Speed is the straight red line and increases steadily. Distance is the curved yellow line. It will increase at an ever greater rate.

ACCELERATORS, PARTICLE

Particle accelerators (pärt′ i kəl ik sel′ ə rāt′ ərz) are machines used by nuclear scientists to speed up the flow of nuclear particles. These high-speed particles are then sent smashing into a target consisting of a small amount of an element. This process is called bombardment. A nuclear reaction results, and the fast-moving particles either split the atoms in the target or join with those atoms to form new elements. Particle accelerators are usually very large. Stanford University in California has a linear accelerator (one that runs in a long, straight line) with a tube that is 3.2 km [2 mi] long. The European Organization for Nuclear Research (CERN), near Geneva, Switzerland, has a circular accelerator that is 2.2 km [1.4 mi] in diameter.

There are three main types of accelerators: electrostatic, linear, and circular. The electrostatic (also called a Van de Graff generator) uses very high voltage and gives only a single impulse, or push, to each particle. Linear accelerators use electromagnetic fields to give particles one boost after another as they move through long straight pipes called drift tubes. Circular accelerators, including cyclotrons and synchrotrons, use powerful magnets to bend the speeding particles into a circular path. Successive jolts of electricity make them go faster and faster. The energy acquired by the speeding particles in these machines can amount to more than 1 trillion electron-volts. The accelerators may use as much electricity as an entire town.

Lord Rutherford, a British physicist, developed the first artificial nuclear reaction in 1919. He bombarded nitrogen nuclei with naturally produced alpha particles. But naturally produced particles do not have enough speed to be able to cause nuclear reactions with most nuclei. Rutherford could go no further with the experiment. Then, in 1931, Dr. E. O. Lawrence, of the University of California, invented the cyclotron. It was a circular accelerator that greatly speeded up the motion particles. It made a new range of experiments possible. A year later, in 1932, John Cockroft and Ernest Walton, two British physicists, built the first linear accelerator. Using the new linear accelerator, the two scientists were able, for the first time in history, to accelerate particles to speeds that would allow them to split the nucleus of an atom, a process called fission. Cockroft and Walton bombarded the element lithium with a beam of protons, splitting the lithium nucleus into two halves. The nuclear fragments created in this way were themselves the nuclei of helium atoms.

Protons, electrons, and the nuclei of the lighter elements are the particles most often accelerated. They are aimed at a target at the end of the accelerator. This target is a nucleus of another element. When the target nucleus absorbs the bombarding particles, a different element is formed. This is called transmutation. Scientists have produced several new artificial elements this way. Some of them are: neptunium, fermium, berkelium, and mendelevium. Experimenters have even been able to turn lead into gold. However, the change from lead into gold is much too costly for practical use.

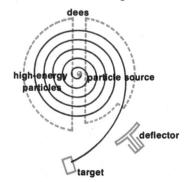

This diagram shows how a cyclotron works. The two "dees" are hollow vacuum tubes, shaped like capital letter Ds back to back. They carry opposite electrical charges. The charge on each dee is reversed every millionth or so second. Charged particles at the center are attracted to the dee with the opposite charge. But, since the charge on the dee changes continuously, the particles move outwards. They move in a spiral at ever greater speed. Finally, they are deflected by an electrode, which causes them to hit the target.

dees

high-energy particles

particle source

deflector

target

Bubble chambers are used to detect collisions between subatomic particles that have been boosted to enormously high speeds in accelerators. Shown is a large bubble chamber operated by CERN in Switzerland.

Below is the Stanford Linear Accelerator Center (SLAC) at Menlo Park, California. The accelerator is two miles long and can accelerate electrons and positrons to higher energies than have ever been achieved before.

Many other exciting discoveries have been made in accelerator experiments. Mesons, particles that are lighter than protons but heavier than electrons, are one such find. Scientists believe that one form of meson is responsible for the tremendous force that binds protons and neutrons together in the nucleus. The neutrino, a particle that apparently has no mass when at rest, was another such discovery. Since the energy content of a neutrino at rest is apparently zero, according to Albert Einstein's famous equation, $E = mc^2$, its mass at rest must also be zero.

The study of how particles react when bombarded is called particle physics or high energy physics. A high energy physics center with a particle accelerator is a large, busy place containing some of the most complicated and expensive equipment in the world. The hundreds of scientists and technicians are carefully protected from the dangerous particle beams and the intense electrical voltages.

Thousands of reactions from bombardments must be analyzed before scientists can be sure of the results. Three kinds of detectors or chambers are used in this work. Bubble chambers are tanks containing a liquid that is near its boiling point. Particles from a nuclear reaction, made to travel through this liquid, leave behind a visible trail of bubbles. Cloud chambers direct particles through a cloud of cooled gases, causing the particles to leave visible condensation trails. In spark chambers, high-energy particles leave a trail of sparks as they ionize air or gas between electrified plates whose charge keeps changing. The trails in all three kinds of chambers are photographed automatically and analyzed by computers. *See also* NUCLEUS (ATOMIC).

W.R.P./J.T.

ACCOMMODATION (ə käm′ ə dā′ shən) The automatic adjustment in eyes which allows them to focus on an object is called accommodation. The ciliary muscle controls the thickness of the eye lens. The lens bends

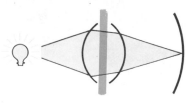

When we look at objects, our eyes often must accommodate so that we can see these objects clearly. The light from nearby objects must be bent by the lens of each eye in order to focus the light on the retina. The lens accommodates by becoming rounder.

the light entering the eye. Light rays from the object of interest focus on the sensitive retina on the inside rear surface of the eyeball.

S.R.G./S.S.B.

ACETATE *See* ACETIC ACID.

ACETIC ACID (ə sēt′ ik a′ səd) Acetic acid is an organic acid with a strong, vinegar-like smell. Its chemical formula is CH_3COOH. Pure acetic acid is a colorless liquid that corrodes other objects. The boiling point of acetic acid is 118°C [244°F]. Its freezing point is 17°C [62°F]. In a cool atmosphere, the pure acid turns solid. It forms white, icy crystals. The pure form is known as glacial acetic acid.

Acetic acid is formed in the fermentation process used for making vinegar. Vinegar contains about 5% acetic acid. However, it is most often produced by the use of chemicals. Acetic acid is used to make acetates. Acetates are the substances that acetic acid forms with bases or alcohols. The most important acetates are cellulose acetate and vinyl acetate. They are both used in plastics.

Acetic acid is also used as a chemical solvent, food preservative, and in photographic processing.

J.J.A./J.M.

ACETONE (as′ ə tōn′) Acetone is a colorless liquid with a sweet odor. Its chemical formula is CH_3COCH_3. It is also called dimethyl ketone or propanone. Acetone has a boiling point of 56.5°C [133.7°F]. Its freezing point is −95°C [−139°F]. Acetone can be obtained from the distillation of wood, or from the bacterial fermentation of molasses. It can also be made by other chemical methods.

Acetone dissolves many substances. It is used as a solvent in industry. It is also used in the making of acetate rayon, thread, photographic film, and fingernail polish. J.J.A./J.M.

ACETYLENE (ə set′ əl ən) Acetylene is a colorless, poisonous gas, with a chemical formula of C_2H_2. It burns easily. Acetylene is made from calcium carbide and water. Pure acetylene has very little smell. The acetylene produced in industry has a strong, unpleasant odor. Acetylene dissolves easily in acetone. It does not dissolve as well in water or alcohol. It dissolves more easily at low temperatures and under high pressure. Acetylene cannot be compressed without danger of explosion. It is stored and transported in cylinders containing acetone.

The main use of acetylene is in the welding and cutting of metals with an oxyacetylene torch. When acetylene burns, it reaches a temperature of 3,500°C [6,332°F] or more. At this high temperature, it can cut metal that is several inches thick. Chemists often call acetylene ethyne. Other substances that are made from acetylene include vinyl plastics, synthetic rubber and fibers, and many organic chemicals. Acetylene was once commonly used for light in portable lamps, buoys, and road signals. J.J.A./J.M.

ACHILLES TENDON (ə kil′ ēz ten′ dən) The Achilles tendon is located on the lower leg of humans. It connects the gastrocnemius muscle to the heel bone of the foot. It is the largest tendon in the human body. The gastrocnemius muscle and the Achilles tendon move the foot up and down.

The tendon gets it name from Greek mythology. It was said that the Greek hero Achilles could not be harmed or wounded

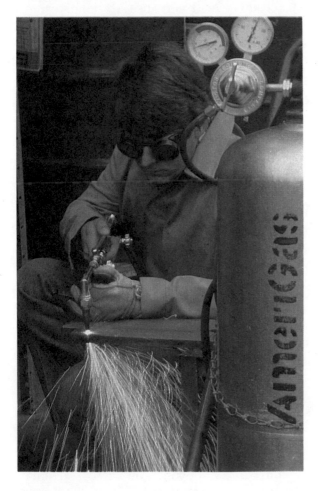

This oxyacetylene torch provides enough heat energy to cut through the sheet of metal.

The Achilles tendon connects the large calf muscle of the leg to the heel bone of the foot.

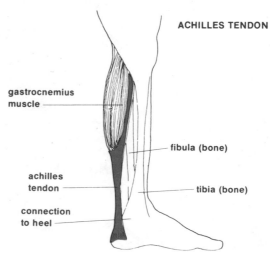

ACHILLES TENDON

gastrocnemius muscle

fibula (bone)

achilles tendon

tibia (bone)

connection to heel

anywhere on his body, except on the heel of his foot. That is where the Achilles tendon connects to the bone.   s.r.g./j.j.f.

ACHROMATIC LENS *See* ABERRATION.

ACID (as′ əd) An acid is a sour-tasting substance. Lemon juice has a sour taste because of the citric acid it contains. The sour taste of vinegar comes from its acetic acid. The acids in lemon juice and vinegar are diluted with water. They cause no harm to the body. However, other acids can be dangerous. Hydrofluoric acid (HF) is so powerful it can corrode and dissolve metals and glass.

There are two main chemical groups of acids. They are inorganic acids and organic acids. Organic acids contain carbon. Inorganic acids do not contain carbon. All acids have one thing in common. When they dis-

Safety precautions are needed when working with strong acids. This worker, repairing the base of an acid reaction tower, is protected by acid-proof clothing that includes a helmet and visor.

solve in water, they release hydrogen ions (H⁺). Hydrogen ions are hydrogen atoms with a positive electric charge. Acids that make a large number of hydrogen ions in water are strong acids. Hydrochloric acid, nitric acid, and sulfuric acid are examples of strong acids. Acids that make few hydrogen ions in water are weak acids. Acetic acid, citric acid, and carbonic acid are examples of weak acids.

With the strongest acids, such as hydrochloric acid (HCl), all the molecules split up to give hydrogen ions. Chemists can measure the strength of hydrogen ions in a solution. This is called the pH of a solution. Acids have a pH of 0 to 7. Acids with a low pH number, such as 2, are stronger than acids with a high pH number such as 6.

One way of telling whether or not a substance is an acid is to use an indicator. An indicator is an object that turns a certain color in an acid. Litmus paper is an indicator that turns from blue to red in an acid. No one should ever taste unknown solutions to find out whether or not they are acids. Some acids burn the tongue. Other acids are poisonous. Certain acids burn and wound the skin.

Many foods turn sour when they spoil. Their starches and sugars break down into acids. For example, when milk turns sour, some of the milk sugar is changed to lactic acid. Butter that spoils contains butyric acid.

If certain metals, like iron or zinc, are added to acid solutions, the metal dissolves. Hydrogen gas (H₂) is also produced from this reaction. This happens because the atoms from the metal and the hydrogen ions from the acid combine. Together they make hydrogen gas and metal ions. The metal ions combine with the acid to produce a salt. In this way, the metal replaces the hydrogen in the acid. For example, if zinc (Zn) is added to hydrochloric acid (HCl), zinc chloride (ZnCl₂), a salt, and hydrogen gas (H₂) are produced.

Our lives depend on acids. Human stomachs contain diluted hydrochloric acid. This acid works with enzymes to digest the

A TABLE OF ACIDS

their uses and where they occur naturally

INORGANIC ACIDS

Name of acid		Important Uses	Formula and physical state, as used
	HYDROCHLORIC	Dissolving metals and preparing chlorides	HCl, gas, dissolved in water
	SULPHURIC	Making explosives, fertilizers, laboratory chemicals, and in petroleum refining and metal cleaning	H_2SO_4, liquid
	PERCHLORIC	A very powerful oxidizing agent used in laboratories. Explosive when undiluted	$HClO_4$, liquid, used diluted with water
	NITRIC	Making fertilizers, explosives, plastics, dyes, and rocket fuels. A strong laboratory oxidizing agent	HNO_3, liquid
STRONG	HYDROBROMIC	A laboratory chemical for making bromides	HBr, gas, dissolved in water
	SULPHUROUS	Bleaching agent, fruit preservative, and laboratory reducing	SO_2, gas, dissolved in water
	ORTHOPHOSPHORIC	Making fertilizers, and in food, sugar, and textile manufacture	H_3PO_4, liquid
	HYDRIODIC	Making organic chemicals and, in laboratories, for iodides	HI, gas, dissolved in water
	HYDROFLUORIC	Etching glass	HF, liquid, diluted with water
	BORIC	Making glass and enamels, medicines, and eyewashes	H_3BO_3, solid or dissolved in water
WEAK	CARBONIC	Laboratory chemical. Carbonates are found in many rocks	CO_2, gas, dissolved in water
	HYPOCHLOROUS	A laboratory oxidizing agent	HClO. A solution in water
	HYDROCYANIC (Prussic acid—extremely poisonous)	Making plastics and rubber. Fumigating buildings to kill rats and insects	HCN, liquid. Solutions in water also used

ORGANIC ACIDS (strongest down to weakest)

Name of acid	Important Uses	Physical state at room temperature	Where found naturally
SULPHONIC (ACIDS)	Making dyes and drugs	Liquids and solids	—
TRICHLOROACETIC	A weedkiller used for grasses	Liquid	—
OXALIC	Making textiles, leather, and organic chemicals. A stain remover	Solid	Rhubarb leaves
PHTHALIC (ACIDS)	Making dyes and plastics	Solids	—
TARTARIC	Making baking powders and medicines. An oxidizing agent	Solid	Grape juice and other juices
SALICYLIC	Making aspirin and other antirheumatic medicines. A food preservative	Solid	Oil of wintergreen
CITRIC	Making medicines and soft drinks	Solid	Citrus fruits (lemons, oranges). Important biochemical in metabolism
MALIC	In medicines	Solid	Unripe apples and gooseberries
FORMIC	Making textiles, leather, and chemicals	Liquid	Nettle, ant, and caterpillar stings
LACTIC	Making textiles, and in food	Solid	Sour milk and tired muscles
BENZOIC	Soft drinks and cosmetics. Preserving food	Solid	Resins, cranberries and horses' urine
SUCCINIC	—	Solid	Amber and fossil wood. Important in metabolism
ACETIC	Making vinegar, plastics, solvents, drugs, and dyes	Liquid	—
PHENOL (carbolic acid)	Making dyes, disinfectants, and organic chemicals	Solid	—

"BIOLOGICAL" ACIDS

Types of acids	Names of acids	Physical state as prepared	Where found naturally
AMINO ACIDS	20 amino acids are found in living organisms	Liquids and solids	These are the acids which link together to make proteins, which make muscle
NUCLEIC ACIDS	DNA (deoxyribonucleic acid) and RNA (ribonucleic acids)	Glassy liquids or solids	These are the huge molecules which, together with proteins, make up the chromosomes in all living organisms

food we eat. Amino acids are essential to all kinds of life. Human beings need eight special amino acids to stay alive. Ascorbic acid from fruits and vegetables is also important. Ascorbic acid is vitamin C. If a person doesn't eat foods that contain vitamin C, he will become sick with the disease called scurvy. Most of the acids that are important in biology are weak organic acids.

Acids are important in industry. Millions of tons of sulfuric acid are made every year. Sulfuric acid is used to dissolve the rust and scale on iron. It cleans the iron completely. This type of cleaning is called pickling. Acids are also used in making fertilizers, pigments and dyes, plastics, and synthetic fibers. Aqua regia is a mixture of nitric and hydrochloric acids. Aqua regia is used to dissolve gold and platinum. J.J.A./A.D.

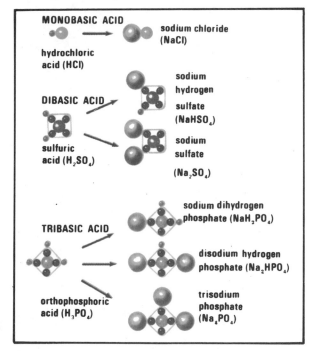

Acids can form one or more kinds of salts. The kind of salt formed depends on the basicity of the acid. A salt is formed when an acid reacts with a base. Common table salt results from the reaction of monobasic hydrochloric acid and sodium hydroxide. The diagram shows examples of monobasic, dibasic, and tribasic acids.

ACNE (ak′ nē) Acne is a disorder of the sebaceous glands of the skin. Sebaceous glands normally secrete a fatty substance called sebum. If allowed to accumulate, sebum becomes mixed with dust and dirt, causing inflammation and the eruption of pimples. Because acne is related to hormonal changes that occur during adolescence, teenagers often have this problem. Cleanliness and diet also affect the condition of a person's skin. To treat acne, doctors recommend keeping one's face clean and not eating a lot of sweets. Serious cases of acne are treated with prescription drugs. S.R.G./J.J.F.

ACOUSTICS (ə kü′ stiks) Acoustics is the branch of the science and technology of sound that deals with how to use and control sound waves. There are many different subjects studied in acoustics. A large, and very important, part of acoustics is the study of architectural acoustics, or how sound behaves in a room or building.

Architectural acoustics The aim of architectural acoustics is to design rooms with good sound qualities. This is very important in buildings such as concert halls and cinemas. In these buildings, the sound should be neither too loud nor too soft. People expect to be able to hear clearly wherever they are sitting in the auditorium. The building has to be designed with this in mind.

In a room, some materials, such as plaster, reflect sound. Other materials, such as carpets, absorb sound. Clothing, draperies, and human bodies also absorb sound. In an auditorium, there has to be just the right balancing and placing of materials. This ensures that the sound is evenly spread.

Sound has two properties that are very important in acoustics. These properties are echo and reverberation. An echo is a sound that has been reflected from a surface. Materials that reflect sound well produce strong echoes. In an auditorium, we hear the sound both directly from the stage and from the echo. Since the echo has bounced off a surface, it has traveled further than the direct

The ancient Greeks, with good acoustic common sense, realized that people are efficient sound absorbers. Their bodies will block sound from one another. Accordingly, the Greeks designed their theaters so that members of the audience would not screen one another. A notable example is this theater located at Epidaurus, an ancient seacoast town. This structure was designed about 340 BC by Polyclitus, a leading sculptor of that period.

sound. This means that it reaches our ears after the direct sound. In a well-designed room, the echo and the direct sound are heard almost at the same time. The sound is then clearly heard. In a poorly designed room, the time difference between the two is quite long. Then the echo gets mixed up with later sounds from the stage.

A reverberation is a closely grouped series of echoes. Each echo is quieter than the one before. Rooms could be built with sound-absorbent materials to remove reverberations and echoes. But then the sound in such a room would have a dead quality. A certain amount of reverberation is necessary for the quality of

the sound. In general, the reverberations should last for between 1 and 2.5 seconds. This is called the reverberation time. It is the time taken for all echoes to die away. Rooms used for music should have a slightly longer reverberation time than rooms used for speech.

Another problem in designing an auditorium is the volume of sound. People sitting at the back should be able to hear clearly. Sometimes this means that the sound has to be amplified by loudspeakers. Often this is not very satisfactory. Loudspeakers rarely reproduce the sound accurately.

The pitch, or frequency, of a sound must also be considered. Sounds with different pitch can be reflected from surfaces in different amounts. Resonance must also be avoided. This causes one particular frequency to sound much louder than the others. Both these effects cause either the high or the low frequencies to sound too loud. If the high

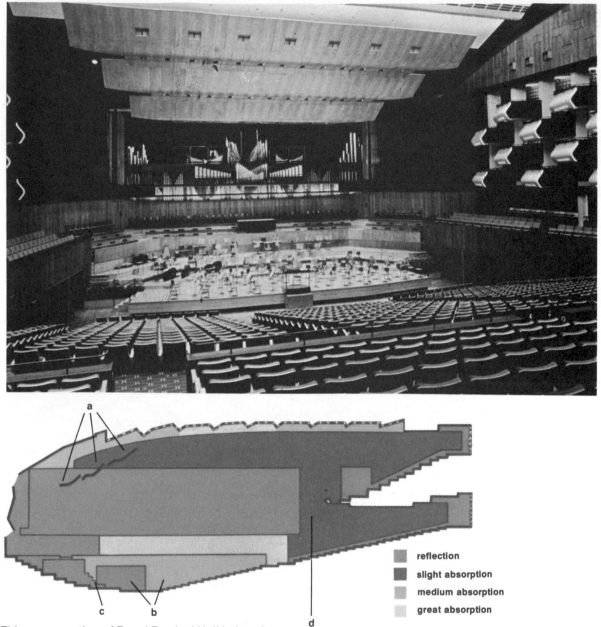

a

c   b   d

reflection
slight absorption
medium absorption
great absorption

This cross section of Royal Festival Hall in London shows its acoustical design. The canopy (a), platform (b), and orchestra (c) reflect sound waves outward. But the walls (d) absorb sound and so prevent confusing sound reflections. The audience also absorbs much of the sound produced in this hall.

frequencies are too loud, the sound has a shrill, thin quality. If the low frequencies are too loud, the sound is dull and muffled.

The first people to build their theaters acoustically were the ancient Greeks. They placed their audiences on steep hillsides where sound could travel to them directly. Their theaters were called amphitheaters. The stage was at the bottom of rows of seating that were steeply inclined. Every member of the audience could see and hear well. This idea was copied by the Romans. The Hollywood Bowl, in California, is a modern-day amphitheater.

Acoustic design is not yet perfectly understood. The acoustics of a building are often tested as the building is being constructed. Sometimes the design of the building must be changed or different materials must be used. Acoustical engineers often use scale models of buildings or rooms to test the acoustics.

Other branches of acoustics Although architectural acoustics is an important field, the science of acoustics has other, very different branches.

In communications acoustics, engineers are trying to build machines that can speak and hear. This is a very difficult task. Human speech is a complicated mixture of frequencies. Our brains can easily put all these different frequencies together to hear a spoken word. Machines cannot do this yet, but progress is being made. Such machines would be very useful in banks. In a bank, the identity of a customer is checked by his signature. It is very difficult for anybody to copy another person's signature. But it is not impossible. A better method of checking a person's identity would be from the pattern of his speech. This pattern is unique and it is impossible for anyone else to copy. A machine that could check this pattern would be very useful in a bank.

Machines that can speak and hear can also be very useful in the field of computers. A number of computer functions can now be activated by human speech. And computers have the ability to talk to people through voice synthesizers.

Ultrasonics is another important branch of acoustics. Ultrasonics is the study of sound waves that have too high a frequency to be heard. Normally a sound wave travels smoothly through an object. However, if the object has a crack in it, the waves are reflected and refracted. This is used to detect cracks in engine parts and in other things. Ultrasonic waves are used since they are refracted through a larger angle than sound waves. This makes the cracks more easily detectable. This method is used especially to test spacecraft components, where their reliability is very important. *See also* ECHO; FREQUENCY; SOUND; RESPONSE.   M.E./R.W.L.

ACROMEGALY (ak′ rō meg′ ə lē) Acromegaly is a disease that causes certain parts of the body to grow larger than they normally would. The parts of the body usually affected are the hands, feet, head, and face. Growth is caused and controlled by the production of a growth hormone by the pituitary gland. If too much of this hormone is released while a person is growing, he or she appears normal, but is very large. This is what has happened to many of the professional basketball players who are over 2.1 m [7 ft] tall. If too much growth hormone is released after a person is full grown, acromegaly will cause the body to become deformed. Acromegaly can be stopped either by x-ray treatment of the pituitary gland or by its removal.   S.R.G./J.J.F.

ACRYLIC (ə kril′ ik) An acrylic is a fiber made from chemicals. It can also be a plastic.

This modern sculpture was constructed of acrylic and lacquer.

Acrylics are made from substances produced from acrylic acid. These substances are bonded by themselves or with other substances. (*See* POLYMERIZATION.)

Acrylic fibers are made into many kinds of fabrics. These fabrics are used in blankets, carpets, underwear, and knitwear. Common trade names for some acrylic fibers are Acrilan, Creslan, Zefran, and Orlon.

A widely used acrylic plastic is polymethyl methacrylate. Plastics made from this substance are better known as Plexiglas and Lucite. They are important because they are transparent. They are used as windows, television lenses, outdoor signs, automobile taillights, salad bowls, surgical tools, and costume jewelry.

Although acrylics stand up well under bad weather conditions, they are softer than glass. That explains why they are easily scratched.

J.J.A./J.M.

ACTH *See* ADRENAL GLANDS.

ACTINIUM (ak tin′ ē əm) Actinium is a very rare, metallic element. Its symbol is Ac. It has an atomic number of 89 and an atomic weight of 227. The melting point of actinium is 1,922°F (1,050°C) and it boils at about 5,792°F (3,200°C). Actinium is found in uranium ores. It was discovered by André Debierne in 1899.

Actinium is a radioactive element. (*See* RADIOACTIVITY.) It has a number of different isotopes. Most of them decay very quickly, giving off beta rays and alpha rays. The most common isotope of actinium is actinium-227. It is quite stable and has a half-life of 21.6 years. Actinium-227 is used to produce neutrons.

M.E./J.R.W.

ADAMS, JOHN COUCH *See* NEPTUNE.

ADAPTATION (ad ap tā′ shən) Adaptation is a process in which living things change with new environmental conditions. There are two kinds of adaption. One occurs to an individual organism during its lifetime. The other occurs, through evolution, to a group of organisms over thousands or millions of years.

If a man begins a new nighttime job—after working during the day all of his life—he must adapt to his new way of life. To begin with, he may have difficulty sleeping during the day. After a while, however, he sleeps easily. He has adapted. This is an example of individual adaptation.

The giraffe provides an example of how a group evolves as individual members adapt to changing conditions. Thousands of years ago, giraffes, like horses, had short necks and ate grass. During a long dry period, much of the grass in Africa died. Some giraffes, the ones with the longest necks, adapted by eating the leaves of trees. They survived and reproduced. Their offspring had long necks also. As time went on, the trees grew higher, and giraffes had to reach higher up to eat the leaves. In this way, long-necked giraffes always had an advantage. The result was that the giraffes today have much longer necks than giraffes had thousands of years ago.

Some living things are able to adapt easily, while others cannot. Perhaps dinosaurs became extinct because they could not adapt

Adaptation to particular habitats is found in all living things. Plants adapt to the amount of water in the environment. Oak trees, on the left, live in a moist climate. Their green leaves require much water to carry on photosynthesis. The desert cactus shown on the right would lose too much water if its leaves were broad, so it has spines instead.

to sudden or rapid changes in the climate of the earth. Humans are very adaptable. With special equipment, they can live anywhere on earth. They can even visit the moon.

S.R.G./R.J.B.

The beaks of birds are adapted for particular ways of feeding. Birds that live on or near water have weed-scooping mouth parts. The long beak of the hummingbird is specialized for nectar sipping. The woodpecker and kingfisher have spears that stab their prey. The crossbill digs seeds out of pine cones with ease.

flamingo

crossbill

white-fronted goose

common kingfisher

pufflegs hummingbird

great spotted woodpecker

ADDER (ad′ ər) The adder is a poisonous snake belonging to the family Viperidae. It is sometimes called the viper. There are many species of adders found in Europe, Asia, and Africa. Adders grow from 0.3 m [1 ft] to 1.8 m [6 ft] in length. Their colors vary with species and geographical location. The adder kills its prey by biting. It injects venom with its two long fangs. After the animal dies, the adder swallows it whole. An adder can kill as soon as it is born or hatches from its egg. Adders found in the colder regions of Europe and Asia spend the winters in hibernation.

One of the best-known adders is the European viper. It lives in Europe and Asia and as far north as the Arctic Circle. It hunts at night for rodents, birds, lizards, and amphibians. The European viper grows to a length of 0.6 m [2 ft]. Its bite can be fatal to humans. The puff adder of Africa is one of the largest, growing to a length of 1.35 m [4.5 ft]. As thick as a person's arm, it too has a poisonous bite.

S.R.G./C.J.C.

The adder, or European viper, is about two feet long. It is recognized easily by its characteristic zigzag stripe. Like other vipers, this snake has poison fangs set on a movable bone at the front of its upper jaw. It raises this jaw to inject its poison.

ADDICTION (ə dik′ shən) Addiction is a harmful physical dependence that can result from regular use of certain drugs, such as heroin and other narcotics. Although a person may become psychologically dependent on the caffeine in coffee or nicotine in cigarettes, such habits can be broken. Drug addiction is a much more difficult habit to cure because, with development of addiction, changes in the body's chemistry produce unpleasant, even painful, symptoms when the drug is withheld. The problems of addiction are both medical and sociological. The addict's health suffers, and the illegal trade in drugs gives rise to many other criminal activities.

ADDISON'S DISEASE (ad' ə sənz diz ēz') Addison's disease causes weakness, digestive problems, heart problems, and a brown coloring of the skin. It occurs when a person's adrenal glands do not produce enough cortical steroid hormones. These hormones normally keep salts in the bloodstream at the right level. They also regulate the body's metabolism. Addison's disease is treated by taking the hormone cortisol. The disease is named after Thomas Addison, who first described it in 1855.   S.R.G./J.J.F.

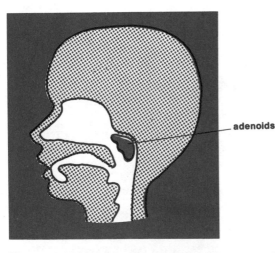

The normal function of adenoids is the protection of the throat. When infected, they can be removed.

ADENOID (ad' ən ȯid') The adenoids are found in humans at the back of the nasal passage leading to the throat. They are lymphatic glands which produce mucus for the throat. They protect the throat against infection. However, the adenoids often become infected and swollen. This causes a sore throat and makes breathing difficult. It may also lead to loss of hearing. When this happens, a doctor will often remove the adenoids. The adenoids are similar to tonsils in that a person can stay healthy without them.

S.R.G./J.J.F.

ADHESION (ad hē' zhən) Adhesion is the electrical attraction of molecules of one substance to those of a different substance. The substances will stick together. If you put your finger in a glass of water, some of the water will cling to your finger after you withdraw it. That is adhesion. However, if a person puts a well-greased finger into a glass of water, no water will cling to the finger when he or she removes it. That is because the force of attraction between the molecules of water is greater than the force of adhesion between the molecules of water and the grease on the skin. The attraction of molecules to other molecules of the same substance is called cohesion. *See also* COHESION; SURFACE TENSION.

S.R.G./A.D.

ADHESIVE (ad hē' siv) Adhesives are substances that stick to other substances. They make it possible for materials to be joined together. There are three main types of adhesives: structural, holding, and sealing.

A good example of a structural adhesive is the cement used for making model airplanes. Waterproof glues used in boatbuilding are another example. Holding adhesives include library paste, mucilage, and cellophane tape. They are used to stick paper together or fasten light objects to walls. Sealing adhesives are used to stop leaks in boats or bathroom tiles.

Adhesives used to be made from animal and plant sources. Early glues were made by boiling fish heads and bones. Others were made from gums, like gum arabic, that come from trees. Today most household glues are

water   mercury

Water in a glass tube adheres to the walls of the tube, forming a meniscus, or curved surface, that is concave. This happens because water wets glass. But mercury in a tube forms a convex meniscus. Mercury does not wet the glass. The molecules of mercury attract one another more than they are attracted to the glass. This causes the convex meniscus.

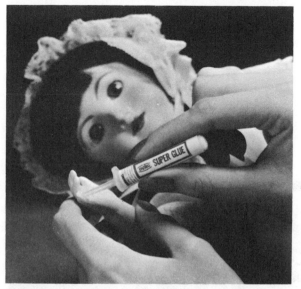

One drop of the so-called super glues may be used to hold together small items or to make bonds that can hold thousands of pounds.

made from chemicals. Of these chemical glues, plastic adhesives make up the largest groups. The epoxy resin types are among the strongest and most useful. The epoxies allow wood, metal, glass, concrete, and ceramics to be joined together. The joints are very strong, usually much stronger than the materials being joined. Epoxies are made in two parts: the base and the catalyst. A chemical reaction occurs when the two are mixed together. The glue must be used quickly or it will harden and become useless.

Rubber serves as the base for a group of adhesives. This group is used for joining leather, rubber, textiles, plastics, and paper. Rubber-based glues and cements are used when the object to be glued will be around water. For example, rubber-based adhesives are used to stick plastic tiles to cement floors in kitchens and bathrooms. Adhesives without a rubber base would not hold down the tiles if water were spilled.

Special household glues have been developed. They are called instant glues. They are cyanoacrylates and require no mixing. They are so strong that a single drop can hold thousands of pounds of weight. Portland cement is another kind of adhesive. It hardens to form a bond between sand and stones to make concrete. *See also* ADHESION; CEMENT.

W.R.P./A.D.

ADLER, ALFRED (1870–1937) Alfred Adler (äd′ lər) was an Austrian psychiatrist and psychologist. He believed that many people lacked self-confidence. In other words, Adler believed that some people thought of themselves as being less important than others. Adler called this an inferiority feeling, which later became known as the inferiority complex. For example, children may suffer from an inferiority complex because they think that their older brothers or sisters have more ability and freedom. Adler believed that such feelings may be the cause of many types of mental illness. (*See* MENTAL HEALTH.) For example, a person who feels inferior may try too hard to prove he or she is not. As a result, the person may become violent or, from lack of confidence, may become a failure. Often, a person who reacts either way refuses to be a member of any group or to have any friends. Adler had great success in guiding children and helping them to overcome feelings of inferiority.

Adler began to work with Sigmund Freud in 1902. In 1911, he left Freud because Freud believed that sexual feelings were the cause of people's psychological problems. Adler strongly disagreed. He came to the United States and gave talks at many colleges and universities. He introduced a movement which is known as Individual Psychology. *See also* PSYCHIATRY; PSYCHOLOGY.

J.J.A./D.G.F.

ADOLESCENCE (ad′ əl es′ əns) Adolescence is the period between childhood and adulthood. It usually occurs between the ages of 12 and 20. Adolescence is sometimes a difficult time of life. Teenagers are no longer children, yet they are not quite adults. They must get used to adult ways. Often, they must begin to take on new duties, such as finding jobs and paying bills. During adolescence, the body matures sexually. This is also called puberty. Boys' and girls' bodies develop so that they can become parents. *See* REPRODUCTION.

S.R.G./J.J.F.

ADRENAL GLANDS (ə drēn′ əl glandz′) The adrenal glands are small, important glands located above the kidneys. They are part of the endocrine system, a group of glands in the body that produces chemicals called hormones. Hormones are released into the bloodstream to control body functions. Each hormone controls a different function.

The adrenal glands have two parts: the adrenal cortex on the outside and the adrenal medulla on the inside. The adrenal cortex produces many hormones that regulate the way the body uses sugar, the body's main source of energy. These hormones also keep the amount of salt in the blood at the right level. If they fail to do this, death will result. The adrenal cortex produces these hormones

This angry serval cat is showing signs of high adrenal gland activity. The adrenal glands of an animal will produce increased amounts of the hormone adrenalin, also called epinephrine, when the animal is afraid, or in a rage. An increased flow of adrenalin causes muscles to tense. This increased muscle tension has raised the hair on this cat's back.

when another hormone, known by its initials ACTH, enters the adrenal glands from the bloodstream. ACTH is produced in the pituitary gland which is located at the base of the brain. The best known hormone of the adrenal cortex is cortisol.

When the adrenal medulla receives a certain signal from the brain, it produces a hormone called adrenalin. Adrenalin gives the body extra energy in times of stress. Someone who has been frightened is able to run faster and longer than usual because of the adrenalin released into his bloodstream. When a person is frightened, but does not run, his hands may shake due to the adrenalin in his blood.

S.R.G./J.J.F.

ADSORPTION *See* ADSORPTION AND ADSORPTION.

AEROBE (ar′ ōb′) An aerobe is an organism that uses the oxygen in the air in order to live and reproduce. In the process of respiration, an aerobe uses the oxygen mostly in order to obtain energy from its food. (*See* RESPIRATION.) Many forms of life, including human beings, are aerobes. The major exceptions are certain microorganisms, such as some types of bacteria, fungi, and protozoa. Aerobic respiration is a more efficient energy conversion process than is the anaerobic style of life, called fermentation. *See also* ANAEROBE; FERMENTATION. A.J.C./E.R.L.

AERODYNAMICS

Aerodynamics (ar′ ō dī nam′ iks) is the study of the flow of air around objects. It is closely related to aeronautics because it studies the flight of airplanes and other machines that are heavier than air.

Four main forces act on a powered airplane in flight: lift, drag, gravity, and thrust. Lift and drag are results of airflow over the plane's surfaces.

Lift The wings lift the airplane. Their shape, angle of attachment, and area are what cause this lift. Seen in cross section, the wing has a rounded nose, a sharply curved upper surface, and a flatter bottom surface. Both surfaces taper to a sharp trailing edge. This is called an airfoil. As the plane flies, the air passing over the top of the wing has a greater distance to travel. Therefore, it must flow faster than the air flowing along the bottom of the wing. The pressure of the faster moving air on top decreases. This creates a suction effect. At the same time, the pressure of the slower-moving air across the underside of the wing increases. These two forces—suction from above and pressure from below—lift the plane as it moves through the air. (*See* BERNOULLI EFFECT.)

The angle at which the wing is attached to the body of the airplane is called the angle of incidence. It also has a part in lift. The front edge of the wing is tilted upward to increase the air pressure on the underside of the wing. The angle at which the air flow hits the wing is called the angle of attack. If it is increased, it increases lift. If the wing is tilted upward too much for a given speed, the airflow across the top of the wing breaks off. The lifting force of

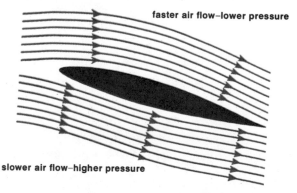

faster air flow–lower pressure

slower air flow–higher pressure

This cross section shows how an airplane wing serves as an airfoil. Air flows faster above the wing than below it. Fast-flowing air exerts less pressure than slower air. The higher pressure below the wing creates lift. Additional lift comes from increasing the angle at which the wing meets air flow.

the wing stops. This is called a stall. If it happens during flight, the airplane must be put into an immediate dive. Then it can pick up enough speed so that air can begin flowing across the top of the wing again. If the stall happens near the ground where there is no room to dive, the airplane may be in danger of crashing.

The shape of the airfoil, the total area of the wings, the angle of attack, the speed of air flow, and the density of the air all contribute to lift. Larger wings provide more lift. Increased speed also provides lift. Lift decreases at very high altitudes where the air is not dense enough to support an airfoil.

Drag   The force that fights against the forward progress of an airplane is called drag. If the shape of the body of the airplane is properly streamlined, the air will flow around it smoothly and cause little drag. A badly shaped body results in poor air flow. As a result, more energy is needed to push the airplane forward.

Skin friction, caused by roughness on the surface of the plane's body, also slows the forward progress of an airplane. Even the smallest bumps on the plane disturb the air. Disturbed air absorbs energy by friction. Skin friction can be reduced by making the surface of the plane's body very smooth. This is why airplanes should have smooth surfaces. It is also why they are constantly cleaned and polished.

Another kind of drag is called induced drag. It is caused by disturbed air at the tips of the wings.

At speeds faster than sound, shock waves develop over the surfaces of the wings. These reduce lift by disturbing the smooth flow of air over the wings and other surfaces. (*See* SUPERSONIC FLIGHT.)

Gravity   Gravity is the force that pulls an airplane downward. The greater the mass, or weight, of the airplane, the more gravity will pull it down. Weight, as a force, is the opposite of lift.

Thrust   Thrust is the force that propels an airplane forward. It is created by the engine, or engines, of the plane. Thrust is the opposite of drag.

Wind tunnels   Airplane engineers test scale models of their designs in wind tunnels. These are large, round chambers with powerful fans blowing air through them in one direction. A model plane is suspended by wires or mounted on a string in the airflow. The designers watch the models through observation windows to see how they react to the air flow. Measurements of all forces on the model are taken with sensitive instruments.

Wind tunnels are also used by automobile engineers and civil engineers to study the effects of air flow. Automobile shapes are designed to reduce drag. Some race cars even have airfoils that keep the car's front wheels on the track at high speeds. Designers of tall buildings and bridges also test models in wind tunnels to be sure the structures will be strong enough to resist high winds.

The theories of aerodynamics date back to

Long bridges are designed on aerodynamic principles to prevent damage by wind.

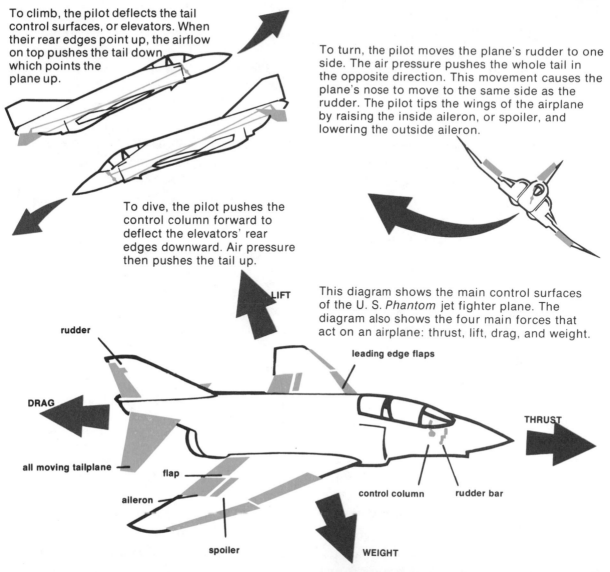

To climb, the pilot deflects the tail control surfaces, or elevators. When their rear edges point up, the airflow on top pushes the tail down, which points the plane up.

To turn, the pilot moves the plane's rudder to one side. The air pressure pushes the whole tail in the opposite direction. This movement causes the plane's nose to move to the same side as the rudder. The pilot tips the wings of the airplane by raising the inside aileron, or spoiler, and lowering the outside aileron.

To dive, the pilot pushes the control column forward to deflect the elevators' rear edges downward. Air pressure then pushes the tail up.

This diagram shows the main control surfaces of the U. S. *Phantom* jet fighter plane. The diagram also shows the four main forces that act on an airplane: thrust, lift, drag, and weight.

LIFT

rudder

leading edge flaps

DRAG

all moving tailplane

flap

aileron

control column

rudder bar

THRUST

spoiler

WEIGHT

Leonardo da Vinci, in the 16th century. He studied birds in flight. He even designed a flying machine that had birdlike wings. Otto Lilienthal provided further research with his study of unpowered flight in the 1880s. Samuel Langley published the first papers on aerodynamics in 1891. The Wright brothers flew the first powered airplane in 1903.

W.R.P./J.VP.

AERONAUTICS (ar´ ə nȯt´ iks) Aeronautics is the science of flight through the air. Aeronautical engineering is a general name for the study, design, building, and operating principles of aircraft.

In the wind tunnel above, a technician is sending a stream of smoke over a test-model car. Information gained on how air flows over a surface can be applied to the design of actual cars.

Aviation is part of aeronautics. It refers most of the time to flight by heavier-than-air machines, such as the airplane and helicopter. These machines are lifted and supported in the air by the motion of air over the fixed or rotating wings.

Aerostatics is the part of aeronautics concerned with lighter-than-air machines, like the balloon or airship. Missiles that fly in the Earth's atmosphere are also included in the field of aeronautics. However, long voyages outside the Earth's atmosphere by craft like satellites belong to the field of astronautics. *See also* AERODYNAMICS; AIRPLANE; AIRPORT.

J.J.A./J.VP.

AEROSOL (ar′ ə säl′) The word aerosol means a mist of tiny drops of liquid suspended in air. Clouds and fog are examples of natural aerosols. Man-made aerosols are very common nowadays. Aerosol cans are often used for spraying paints, perfumes, deodorants, insecticides, and other substances. These cans contain an active ingredient, such as paint, and a propellant. The active ingredient is a liquid and the propellant is a gas in normal conditions. But, because the can is pressurized, the propellant is partly liquid. The liquid propellant and the active ingredient are mixed in the can. When the button on the can is pressed, the pressure of the gas forces

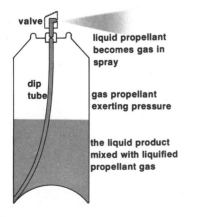

valve

liquid propellant becomes gas in spray

dip tube

gas propellant exerting pressure

the liquid product mixed with liquified propellant gas

Many substances are now packed in aerosol cans. The principle of aerosols is the always the same. The pressure of a gas propellant forces a liquid up a pipe and out through a nozzle as a spray.

the mixture out. The propellant evaporates, leaving a fine spray of the active ingredient.

Until the mid-1970s the most common gas used for a propellant was Freon. Aerosols are now very popular and huge amounts of Freon have been released into the atmosphere. Many scientists believe that this Freon is dangerous. It combines with the ozone in the atmosphere and the ozone layer is destroyed. For that reason, laws were passed to forbid the use of Freon in aerosols. Other propellants are now used. *See also* POLLUTION. M.E./J.T.

AEROSPACE (ar′ ō spās′) Aerospace is a term taken from the words aeronautics and space. Scientists believe that the earth's atmosphere and outer space can be seen together as one vast region. This region, aerospace, includes everything from the surface of the earth outward.

Aerospace also refers to the science of all flight within this region. Aerospace includes aeronautics and astronautics. One of the goals of aerospace science is to study the planets at close range. The science of astronomy is also part of aerospace.

The desire to develop air transportation and to explore space led to the aerospace industry. Some of the things experts in this field have learned are already part of everyday life. More than 200 million passengers are using air transportation each year. Such transportation has proven to be safe, fast, and economical. Television programs from other continents and improved telephone calls across the ocean are sent by satellites. Other satellites, orbiting the earth, provide accurate maps and better weather forecasts. *See also* ASTRONOMY, SPACE TRAVEL. J.J.A./A.D.

AFRICAN VIOLET *See* VIOLETS AND PANSIES.

AGASSIZ, LOUIS (1807–1873) Louis Agassiz (ag′ ə sē) was a Swiss-American naturalist responsible for many important scientific discoveries. He was born in Môtiers, Switzerland and studied medicine in different European schools. He never practiced medicine because he was more interested in nature. He became a professor of natural history at the University of Neuchâtel in Switzerland. Agassiz traveled a great deal and studied fish fossils and the movement of glaciers. He was the first person to propose the idea of continental glaciation. His idea described how, hundreds of thousands of years ago, much of Europe, Asia, and North America was covered by huge sheets of ice. This ice cover was responsible for many valleys, lakes, and mountains.

In 1846, Professor Agassiz came to the United States. He was a very popular public figure and traveled around the country lecturing on natural history. He also taught at Harvard University. He continued to study glaciers, and discovered evidence of a large, prehistoric lake that covered parts of North Dakota, Minnesota, and Canada. This lake is now called Lake Agassiz.   S.R.G./D.G.F.

Louis Agassiz

AGATE (ag′ ət) Agate is a semiprecious mineral from the quartz family. It usually occurs in bright solid colors. Sometimes it has bands or patterns of colors running through it.

Agate probably gets its name from the Achates River in Sicily, where it was first found. Today, it can be found in many places in the world, including the western part of the United States.

Agate is very hard. It is used to make ornaments, brooches, small implements and marbles for children. Some cameos are cut from the onyx variety of agate. A cameo is an ornament showing a raised design in solid color against a lighter background.

W.R.P./R.H.

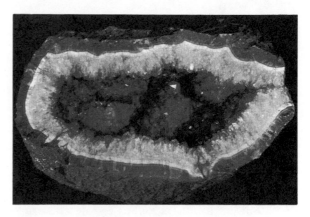

Agate, in a lump of rock called a geode.

AGAVE (ə gäv′ ē) The agave plant belongs to the amaryllis family. It is found in Mexico and the southwestern United States. A waxy coating on its thick, leathery leaves prevents loss of water. This allows the plants to live in hot, dry areas.

Agaves grow bunches of pointed, toothed leaves called rosettes. A flowing stem grows up from the middle of the rosette. Because

Agave parviflora, showing its rosette.

agaves were once believed to take 100 years to produce their first flowers, they have been called century plants. We now know that the plant's first flowers may appear between 8 and 40 years.

Agaves have many uses. The leaves of one species are used in making sisal, a strong fiber used in rope. The roots of others have been used to make soap. The sap of the agave is used in making the alcoholic beverages pulque and mescal. S.R.G./M.H.S.

AGGLOMERATE (ə gläm′ ə rət) Agglomerate is a dark, rough volcanic rock composed of hardened lava mixed with dust and ash, all of which are the products of a volcanic eruption. The volcano is also the source of the heat that serves to bind these materials together to form a rock. *See also* IGNEOUS ROCK. G.M.B./R.H.

AGRICULTURE

Agriculture (ag′ ri kəl′ chər) is the scientific practice of raising plants and animals. When plants and animals are raised by people, they are called crops. Crops may be used for food. Corn is a common food crop. Crops may be used for building. Trees are a building crop. Animals, raised for food or enjoyment, are also a crop. Agriculture continues to improve crops and methods of raising and harvesting them.

History of agriculture Primitive people were probably nomads, roaming around the land to hunt animals and pick fruit. When the food in one region was gone, they moved to another region. When people learned to plant and harvest food, they were able to stay in one place. This allowed the development of villages and the start of civilization. It is generally believed that farming as a regular occupation had already begun in the Middle Eastern area of the world by 6000 BC. While the cultivation of wheat spread in the Mediterranean area, cultivation of rice began in the Far East and cultivation of corn began in the Americas. About the same time, people learned to capture, tame, and raise animals for food. Agriculture began very simply. It developed slowly to the point where farmers learned to improve their crops. Later they built special tools and vehicles to help them.

Modern agriculture Research in genetics, in the early 1900s, did much to improve agriculture. Earlier, in the 19th century, Gregor Mendel had discovered how characteristics of plants and animals are inherited from their parents. By controlling which animals are bred or which seeds are planted, a farmer can get desired characteristics, such as fat pigs or sweet apples. An ear of modern hybrid corn may have twice the number of kernels on it that an ear of wild, uncultivated corn has.

Other aids to modern agriculture have been the gasoline engine, vehicles, and special machinery. Instead of plowing with horses or harvesting by hand, a farmer can use tractors, reapers, and combines. This means he can plant crops more cheaply, more quickly, and more easily. The discovery and use of electricity led to the use of light bulbs and heaters for lighting and warming barns. It led to the use of incubators for hatching chicken eggs, and to the use of refrigerators to keep food from spoiling. Refrigeration allowed the railroads and the growing trucking industry to transport food from the farms to the markets in the cities. This made farming a big business.

Modern technology also helped. Productive farms could be built where crops would not have grown years before. The dry areas of the American Southwest were irrigated by making water from rivers flow to fields. With the abundant sunshine and mild winters, the new crops grow well. (*See* IRRIGATION.)

Advancements in modern science and technology have left their mark on agriculture. Progress in breeding, feeding, pest control, and harvesting methods have been especially important.

Even in the 1700s, man realized that plants take valuable chemicals, or nutrients, out of the soil. If too many crops are grown in the same soil, most of the nutrients they need are removed. New crops will not grow well. A system of crop rotation was devised to allow more crops to be grown. In this system, a field is not planted with the same crop every year. Different plants remove different nutrients. Some, like alfalfa, return certain nutrients to the soil. By rotating crops, one nutrient is not totally removed. In addition, every few years certain fields are not planted. This is called letting the fields stand fallow. It allows the nutrients taken from the soil to be replaced before the fields are replanted.

Modern farmers have done even more to return nutrients to the soil. They add them while plowing. This is called fertilizing. Fertilizers can be either animal dung or man-made chemicals. The use of dung to fertilize fields is called recycling. A cow gets nutrients from the soil in the plants it eats. The food it does not digest returns to the soil as dung. The nutrients, originally taken from the soil, have then completed a cycle.

Role of agriculture in society The need for scientific agriculture is increasing. The world's population is growing rapidly. There are more people to feed. However, there is less land for farming because of the growth and spread of cities. More and more good farm land is being used for building houses and factories. In addition, fewer people are farming now. Years ago, farmers' children would also farm. Now many of them are moving to the cities to get jobs. Other people no longer farm because they cannot make enough money. These problems must be solved if we are to meet the food needs of tomorrow. *See also* AGRONOMY; HYDROPONICS; NUTRITION. S.R.G./F.W.S.

AGRONOMY (ə grän′ ə mē) Agronomy is the branch of agriculture that deals with the study of field crops and soil. Agronomists try to improve the quality and yield of crops such as rice, wheat, corn, and sorghum. They also learn how to control pests, diseases, and weeds. Because agronomists are concerned about the quality of the soil, they try to find ways to improve it and to prevent soil erosion. S.R.G./F.W.S.

AILANTHUS (ā lan′ thəs) The ailanthus is a tree originally found in China. It now grows in Europe and North America because people have planted it for its beauty. The tree is also called the tree of heaven. It grows up to 21 m [70 ft] tall. Its leaves resemble ferns. They can reach 1.2 m [4 ft] in length and are made up of 12 to 24 smaller leaves. The flowers of the ailanthus smell bad. The tree blossoms in June. S.R.G./M.H.S.

AIR

Air (ar) is the mixture of gases that surrounds the earth. It is invisible, tasteless, and has no smell. Air extends great distances above the earth. One half of the air, by weight, is within 5.63 km [3.5 mi] of the earth's surface. The other half is spread over hundreds of kilometers beyond that. The layer of air surrounding the earth makes life possible. It is prevented from escaping into space by gravity.

Composition of air Air is a mixture of gases. Nitrogen makes up about 78% of the air, oxygen 21%, and argon almost 1%. More accurately, these gases make up 99.77% of the air. The remaining gases include tiny percentages of carbon dioxide, helium, krypton, neon, ozone, and xenon.

The amount of carbon dioxide in the air varies from place to place. The highest amounts of carbon dioxide are found in cities and in places like closed rooms. Carbon dioxide is a very important gas. It is used by green plants in photosynthesis.

Air also contains moisture in the form of water vapor, which is a gas. The amount of water vapor in the air depends upon the temperature. Warm air can hold much more water vapor than cold air.

Dust in the air serves as a center around which water vapor collects. This dust may come from dust storms, automobile exhaust, or smoke from factories. Dust also includes plant pollen, bacteria, and tiny salt particles.

When warm air cools, it may reach dewpoint. Dewpoint is the temperature at which the air is holding all the water it possibly can. The term relative humidity is used to describe the amount of water vapor in the air compared to the amount of water vapor the air can hold at a given temperature. When air reaches dewpoint, the relative humidity is 100%. (*See* HUMIDITY.)

Cooling may also cause water vapor to surround specks of dust to form tiny water droplets. A mass of these droplets forms a cloud. If the conditions are right, clouds may produce rain or snow. High up in the atmosphere, where it is very cold, water vapor may become ice crystals by a process called sublimation. A mass of ice crystals forms cirrus clouds high in the atmosphere. (*See* CLOUDS.)

The air surrounding the earth is divided into layers. From the earth's surface to about 11.3 km [7 mi] up is the troposphere. This is where almost all of the earth's weather occurs. Above this layer are the stratosphere and the ionosphere. The exosphere is where the air thins out into space. (*See* ATMOSPHERE.)

Some important properties of air are shown in these pictures. Warm air holds water vapor, which on rising to cooler heights forms clouds such as those shown at the left. Air filters light, which at sunset travels through more atmosphere than earlier in the day. Because the red part of sunlight is more penetrating than the other parts, we see sunsets as having reddish colors.

Air weight and pressure The force of gravity holds the air and gives it weight. At sea level, 0.03 cu m [1 cu ft] of air weighs 0.037 kg [0.081 lbs]. However, the hundreds of kilometers of air above the earth weigh so much that the total force on 1 sq m [10.7 sq ft] of surface is about 10,253 kg [22,604 lbs]. Air pressure is the measure of the force of air on a given area. Air pressure at the earth's surface is equal in all directions. People do not feel this pressure because their bodies are supported by equal pressure on the inside of their bodies. In the atmosphere, air pressure varies and is measured by instruments called barometers. Weather forecasts are based on changes in barometric pressure. (*See* WEATHER.)

Air pressure decreases above sea level. At 5,486 m [18,000 ft] high, the pressure is one-half as great as it is at the earth's surface. For this reason, airplanes have pressurized cabins to make flying more comfortable. Air pressure is used as a force in pumps. Air pressure is what keeps automobile tires from going flat.

Air resistance People move through air easily, as they do in walking. However, a piece of paper dropped in the air floats slowly to the ground. The falling of the paper is slowed down because of the air resistance acting on the large surface area of the paper. A bullet moves quickly through the air. Its smooth surface and pointed end reduce air resistance.

Air motion Although it may seem to be motionless on a hot summer's day, air is never still. Molecules of air are in constant motion. Large masses of air also move. This motion is measured as wind. The sun provides the energy that causes the air to move. Because air is always moving, the weather is always changing. (*See* AIR MASS; WIND.)

Air pollution Air pollution is a serious problem. Automobiles and factories pour smoke, dust, and harmful gases into the air. Radioactive particles and gases also pollute the air. A lot of dust helps to form smog. Air pollution also reduces the amount of sunshine. Sulfur dioxide in the air corrodes metal and stonework. In the United States, the damage to crops and livestock by air pollution amounts to over $100,000,000 in one year.

Air motion, or wind, keeps kites aloft.

Many scientists and government agencies are working to control air pollution. In the United States, public health is protected by government standards that limit the amount of pollution produced by cars and factories. Since every living thing depends on air to survive, making sure the air is clean helps to make sure that healthy life in all forms will continue.   J.J.A./C.R.

AIR-CUSHION VEHICLE (ar kùsh′ ən vē′ ik əl) An air-cushion vehicle, also called a Hovercraft or surface-effect ship, can hover over the ground on a cushion of air. It can travel over any fairly flat surface, either earth or water.

Most air-cushion vehicles are used for traveling over water. They can move very fast and some have a top speed of 150 km per hour (90 mi per hour). Air-cushion vehicles can travel at these high speeds because they do not move through the water. An ordinary ship travels more slowly. It is slowed down by friction between the hull and the water. (*See* FRICTION.) Air-cushion vehicles skim over the surface on a cushion of air. Air is sucked in through the top of the vehicle by a large fan. The air is then blown through nozzles to the bottom of the Hovercraft. Here it forms a cushion of air.

A Hovercraft floats on a cushion of air. A fan feeds air to the underside of the craft. Openings at the sides provide for the escape of the air currents. An early experimental Hovercraft is shown in the photograph.

Many air-cushion vehicles are surrounded by a "skirt" which reaches down to the water. The "skirt" is called a plenum. It helps to keep the air inside the cushion. This allows the vehicle to ride higher out of the water. An air-cushion vehicle with a plenum can ride over quite high waves without difficulty.

Air-cushion vehicles travel by means of propellers driven by engines. The propellers on the vehicles face backwards. By swiveling the propellers, the vehicle can be steered. Some air-cushion vehicles have large vertical tail fins and are steered by turning the fins to either side.

Because of the high speed at which they can travel, air-cushion vehicles are very useful for carrying passengers and freight between ports. They are only used for fairly short distances, since they cannot, as yet, travel in rough seas. Air-cushion vehicles are also very useful for traveling over swamps.

M.E./R.W.L.

AIR MASS (ar mas) An air mass is a huge body of air. It often extends 1,600 km [1,000 mi] or more across a given area. The higher parts of an air mass are colder than the lower parts. The temperature of air decreases with height. On the same level, the air in one part of the air mass is about the same temperature as the air in other parts of the same mass.

There are two main kinds of air masses. A continental air mass forms over the land. A maritime air mass forms over the sea. Air masses are either warm or cold. A cold air mass is colder than the ground surface over which it moves. A warm air mass is warmer than the surface over which it moves. Cold air weighs more than warm air. Therefore, a cold air mass exerts greater pressure on the earth than a warm air mass does. Cooler air tends to move toward the warmer air because of the difference in pressure.

When a cold air mass meets a warm one, the cold air tends to run under the warm air instead of mixing with it. The line along which this occurs is called a cold front. As the warm air is pushed up, it expands and cools. This causes cloud formations and precipitation, such as rain or snow. Precipitation occurs because warm air holds more water vapor than cool air does. As the warm air grows cooler, the water vapor leaves the air. (*See* CONDENSATION.) It falls to earth in the form of rain, sleet, snow, or a combination of the three. If wind movements cause a warm air mass to overtake a cold air mass, the warm air, weighing less, slides up over the cold. Clouds and precipitation are formed. This is called a warm front.

When an air mass is moving very slowly, its moisture content and temperature are affected by the surface below it. For example, an air mass may take on the coldness of a polar region or the heat of the tropics. The region where an air mass takes on its temperature and moisture is called its source region. The depth to which an air mass is changed by its source region depends upon the length of time the air stays in the source region. It also depends upon the difference between the temperature of the air and that of the underlying surface.

Weather maps use letter symbols to describe the types of air masses. These letters explain where the air mass began, the direction it is taking, and the type of surface over which it is moving. A continental air mass (c) is dry: a tropical air mass (T) is hot; a maritime air mass (m) is humid; and a polar air mass (P) is cold. As an air mass moves from one surface to another, it can change from a warm air mass (w) to a cold air mass (k).

Across the United States, the general movement of air masses is from west to east. A cold air mass moves faster than a warm one. A cold air mass may average 800 to 1,120 km [500 to 700 mi] in a day. The weather depends on the type of air mass and on the action between two or more air masses. With just one air mass, the weather is about the same throughout the area it covers. Differences are caused by changes in the surfaces below, such as lakes, mountains, and valleys. *See also* WEATHER. J.J.A./C.R.

AIRPLANE

An airplane (ar′ plān′) is a heavier-than-air vehicle with fixed wings that flies. There are airplanes with and without engines. The engine, or engines, provides forward motion that causes air to flow over its wings. This creates a lifting force that keeps it in the air. Unpowered airplanes have to be brought into the air by tow before they can glide to earth. (*See* AERODYNAMICS.)

There are three main categories of airplanes: military, commercial, and private. Military planes include fighters, bombers, transports, and trainers. Most are powered by gas turbine jet engines. Commercial planes include passenger and cargo planes used by airlines, as well as planes developed for special uses. For example, some planes are used for spraying insecticides on crops and water solutions on forest fires. Most large commercial planes are powered by jet engines. Some may still have piston engines with propellers, though they are a little old-fashioned. In between these two types are turboprop airplanes which use jet engines and propellers. Private planes are those owned by individuals and companies. They are usually small and carry from one to six people. Most are powered by one or two piston or jet engines.

History The first attempts to fly were made with lighter-than-air vehicles called balloons. The Montgolfier brothers succeeded in making the first balloon flight in 1783, in France, using heated air. Starting 100 years later, Otto Lilienthal of Germany made 2,000 flights in gliders over a 20-year period. Gliders are heavier-than-air, winged vehicles without an engine. They are towed aloft by a winch and cable, or by a powered airplane. Then they are released. They depend upon rising and shifting air currents for lift. In 1903, Orville Wright of the United States made the world's first powered flight at Kittyhawk, North Carolina.

The need for military planes in World War I speeded up airplane development. Progress was rapid. By World War II, in the 1940s, the airplane had become a major weapon. Air speeds in the 480 to 640 kph [300 to 400 mph] range were common. Jet-powered planes were introduced in the late 1940s. They have since come into wide use. Some military and commercial jet planes now fly at supersonic speeds (faster than the speed of sound, 1,220 kph or 760 mph). The French Concorde passenger plane flies at Mach 2.2 (2.2 times the speed of sound, 2,684 kph or 1,672 mph). It is the fastest commercial plane in service.

Other recent developments in airplane design have been VTOL and STOL planes. VTOL (vertical takeoff and landing) planes lift straight up off the ground in a horizontal position, like helicopters, before flying forward. Some VTOLs have two sets of engines. One set lifts the plane off the ground. The other provides the forward thrust. The pilot gradually and smoothly switches from one set to the other when flying height is reached. The process is reversed for landing. Other VTOLs have one engine or set of engines that can pivot 90 degrees. They point up to lift off. Then they move slowly back to normal position for horizontal flight. STOL (short takeoff and landing) planes have powerful engines and high-lift wings that enable them to take off and land on very short runways.

Airplane parts The body of an airplane which contains the pilot cockpit and the passenger compartment is called the fuselage. The wings and tail are attached to it. The engine, or engines, may be mounted in the fuselage or on the wings. Sometimes they are attached beneath the wings on finlike devices called pylons. The landing gear consists of heavy wheels with shock-absorbing supports. The landing gear can be folded up into the plane during flight to reduce air resistance, which would slow the plane. Small private planes often have landing gears that cannot be moved.

The tail surfaces at the rear of the plane and the wings contain movable portions that control the forces on the airplane and the direction of flight. The vertical part of the tail assembly is called the rudder. The horizontal parts, which are like small wings, are called the elevators. Movable parts on the wings include the ailerons, which help control direction. Flaps can be lowered to reduce speed and to increase lift. Spoilers, on top of the wings, help to reduce lift if required. All movable parts are controlled by the pilot from the control center, or flight deck, of the plane.

Wing design varies. Low-speed planes need large, thick wings to achieve sufficient lift. High-speed planes require only small, thin wings. Wings project out at right angles to the fuselage in low-speed planes. They are swept back in a V shape in high-speed planes to reduce drag.

Large passenger planes contain seats for the passengers, kitchens for serving food, and toilets. Baggage is usually stored in spaces below the passenger cabin. The cabin and flight deck areas are pressurized to allow people to breathe at the altitudes where planes fly. This is because large planes fly at heights over 9,000 m [30,000 ft] where the air is too thin for normal breathing.

Airplane engines Gas turbine jet engines and piston engines that drive propellers are the two main sources of power for airplanes. Some jet engines also drive propellers. These are called turboprops. The propeller spins at high speed and creates a lower pressure in front of itself. This sucks the airplane forward. The gas turbine jet engines take in air at the

Shown above is the cabin of a modern jetliner. The instruments include multicolor cathode ray tube (CRT) displays. These displays give pilots more accurate information on the craft's systems.

front end, mix it with fuel, and compress it. The mixture burns and the hot, expanded gases drive the turbine for the compressor and come out the back end at high speed. This provides thrust, or a pushing effect. Turboprop engines combine both methods.

Jet engines create less vibration than piston engines. They are more efficient at high speeds and altitudes. They use kerosene, a fuel that is cheaper than gasoline.

Airplane instruments Modern airplanes are complicated machines. Pilots need many gauges and electronic aids to help fly them. The flight deck of a large passenger plane contains many indicator dials and warning lights. One of the most important instruments is the altimeter. This tells the pilot how high the plane is off the ground. The air speed indicator measures the plane's speed. The artificial horizon shows the position of the plane relative to the horizon. The turn-and-bank indicator shows how much, if at all, the plane

THE MAKING OF CONCORDE

1. The first step in producing an airplane such as the Anglo-French *Concorde* is the preparation of detailed designs by skilled draftsmen.

2. From the plans, a model is built. It is tested in a wind tunnel to find out how the plane will behave in flight.

3. When the tests are completed, work begins on the building of a prototype, which can be tested thoroughly under all kinds of conditions.

4. Here is the *Concorde* in service. Transatlantic flights began in May 1977.

is turning and tilting. In dense clouds and fog, a pilot would not always know which way the plane is heading if it weren't for this instrument. A gyrocompass and various radio devices are necessary for navigation. (*See* GYROSCOPE.)

Most large planes also have an automatic pilot. This is a device operated by a computer. It will fly the plane without the pilot's touching the controls. These autopilots can even control takeoffs and landings. The flight deck also contains many gauges and meters that tell the pilot whether the many pieces of equipment on the plane are operating properly. They measure fuel level, oil pressure, temperatures, thrust, cabin pressure, and electric current. Indicators show whether the landing gear is up or down. The radio equipment allows the pilot to talk to ground controllers and to receive navigation signals.

Airplane construction Early airplanes were made of wood frames covered by fabric and held in shape by wire. After World War I, airplane designers started to use lightweight metals like aluminum, titanium, and magnesium alloys. A thin skin of metal was riveted into place over metal ribs. Strong epoxy glues are now used for some joints, instead of rivets. As planes grew in size, they became heavier. More powerful engines were developed in order to fly the heavier planes.

The use of metals brings with it a problem called metal fatigue. Stress and vibration in flight can cause metal parts eventually to break up. Airplanes must be constantly checked for signs of this trouble. Defective parts must be renewed by aircraft maintenance people.

Designers test scale models in wind tunnels, before the full-sized planes are built. Reactions of the models to high-speed air streams give good indications how full-sized planes will react in flight. This approach helps save a lot of money. It also helps to make airplanes safe. W.R.P./J.VP.

AIRPORT (ar′ pōrt′) An airport is a place where airplanes arrive and depart. Passengers leave and arrive on the airplanes and cargo is loaded and unloaded. Large, jet-powered airplanes require long runways for takeoffs and landings. Big terminal buildings are necessary to handle thousands of passengers and their baggage. Very large airports usually serve several large cities and cover thousands of acres. Hundreds of planes arrive and depart daily. All this traffic must be carefully controlled to avoid delays and accidents. This is done from a control tower. The tower stands high above the ground. Air-traffic controllers, inside the tower, must be able to guide airplanes through their takeoffs and landings.

Large airports are often like small cities. Many have post offices, banks, hotels, restaurants, offices, and many kinds of shops.

This swing-wing military airplane needs a long runway for takeoffs and landings.

Airports also have their own fire and police departments, fuel storage tanks, repair work shops, and storage hangars. Some companies even have their shipping warehouses located at airports.

One of the largest airports in the world is in Grapevine, Texas, midway between the cities of Dallas and Fort Worth. This airport covers 7,200 hectares [18,000 acres]. Its five terminals can handle the arrivals and departures of 90 jumbo jets at the same time. O'Hare International Airport, in Chicago, is the busiest airport in the world. It handles more than 37 million passengers a year.

Small airports that are used only by private airplanes usually cover 20 to 40 hectares [50 to 100 acres]. They do not need all the buildings and services of a large airport. The control tower may be just a small room in a building at ground level.

Runways Early planes were light. Early runways were sometimes just level grass fields. Paved runways became necessary when airplanes became heavier and faster. Today's big jet planes weigh hundreds of tons. They move along runways at speeds of over 160 kph [100 mph]. When they land, they hit the runways hard. The runways take a lot of pounding and must be made of concrete or asphalt. They must have solid foundations and a surface that prevents skidding.

Airplanes take off into the wind in order to get better lift. They also land into the wind in order to have better control as they slow down. (*See* AERODYNAMICS.) Most airports have runways pointing in different directions. This means that there are always runways on which airplanes can go into the wind as they take off and land.

Heavily loaded passenger jets need long runways to gather enough speed to leave the ground. Runways at some large airports are longer than 3,000 m [10,000 ft].

At night, bright lights line the runways so that pilots can find them without trouble. A system of flashing guide lights is set up beyond the runway to help pilots land safely.

Control towers People who work in control towers are called air-traffic controllers. They direct the movements of all planes on the ground and in the air by keeping track of them on large radar screens. Air-traffic controllers tell a pilot, by radio, when and where to taxi or pilot the plane down the runway. At busy hours, when many planes have to take off, as many as 15 jets may have to wait in line to take their turn.

Electronic equipment is used to guide airplanes. Long range radar is used to keep track of planes far away from the airport. This radar is called Ground Control Approach (GCA). When the airplane gets within a few miles of the runway, the air-traffic controller begins to use Precision Approach Radar (PAR). This allows the controller to guide the airplane to within 0.4 km [0.25 mi] of the runway. At that point, the pilot completes the landing. Another electronic aid used in bad weather is the Instrument Landing System (ILS). In this system, radio transmitters located near the runway send guidance signals to the airplane. These signals tell the pilot how to steer the plane for the final approach to the runways. Today, there are also electronic "microwave" landing systems (MLS) that can land the plane fully automatically.

Terminal buildings Terminal buildings vary in size and shape. Most of them are quite large. More than 228 million people fly on the airlines in America each year. Every passenger must pass through terminals. Long, covered walkways lead from the center of some terminals to the gates where airplanes are boarded. At some airports, buses are used to transport passengers to their airplanes. Passengers arriving from another country must pass through customs and passport control. Customs officials check the incoming baggage for taxable items. They also check passengers to be sure no forbidden items are brought into the country. Passport officials check the passports of passengers for personal identification.

Passengers are not allowed to bring guns, knives, or other weapons onto a passenger airplane. Before boarding, they must walk through a detector which triggers a special signal if they are carrying anything made of metal. Luggage is also examined for weapons. This is done to ensure the safety of the passengers. W.R.P./J.VP.

ALBATROSS (al' bə tròs') The albatross is a large seabird that belongs to the family Diomedeidae. It is found mainly south of the equator. The albatross has a long, heavy beak and long, narrow wings which allow it to soar on the wind seemingly without effort for hours. The largest species is the wandering albatross, which has a wingspan of more than 3.4 m [11 ft] and a body 1.2 m [4 ft] long.

Albatrosses have difficulty beginning each flight. They need some wind and must run along the ground or paddle with their webbed feet across the water for a long time before being able to stay in the air.
S.R.G./L.S.

ALBINO (al bī' nō) An albino is a plant or animal that is unable to produce pigment in its cells. Albinism is an inherited disease and is caused by a change in the genes. (*See* GENE; HEREDITY.) Since many animals rely on pigment for protection from the sun and for protective coloration, albino animals are at a definite disadvantage in the wild. (*See* PROTECTIVE COLORATION) Albino animals rarely survive long enough to reproduce.

There are albinos in almost every race of human beings. Many albinos are complete (or true) albinos, and have absolutely no pigment in any of their cells. They have pinkish white skin and white hair. Their eyes appear pink because of the color of the blood vessels. In a normal person, the pigment of the iris (usually

brown or blue) blocks out the color of the blood vessels. (*See* EYE AND VISION.) Since other, light-absorbing pigments are also lacking, an albino is extremely sensitive to bright light such as sunlight.

Some people are partial albinos and lack pigment in some, but not all, tissues and organs. Some animals are also partial albinos.

Some, though not all, plants with white flowers are partial albinos. A complete albino plant lacks even the green pigment chlorophyll. As a result, it is unable to photosynthesize, and dies shortly after food supplies in the seed are used up. (*See* CHLOROPHYLL; PHOTOSYNTHESIS.) *See also* GENETICS; METABOLISM; PIGMENT.

A.J.C./E.R.L.

Albino rabbits have pink eyes. Blood vessels cause the color.

ALCHEMY (al' kə mē) Alchemy was an early form of chemistry. It was widely practised during the Middle Ages. It developed from the ideas of ancient philosophers, such as Aristotle.

An alchemist used chemicals to try and change one thing into another. Alchemists thought that some metals were more perfect than others. They considered gold to be the most perfect metal of all. They tried to discover substances that would make metals more and more perfect. They hoped that the metal would then turn into gold. They called the substance that would do this the philosopher's stone. They thought that if they took the philosopher's stone themselves, they would become better people. They also tried to discover the elixir of life. This was a medicine that was supposed to make people live forever.

Alchemy was related to religion, magic, and astrology. The sun, moon, and planets were linked with different metals. For example, alchemists linked gold with the sun and silver with the moon.

People lost faith with alchemy in the 1600s. It is now thought to be unscientific. However, the alchemists' methods of heating and mixing substances led to modern chemistry.   M.E./R.W.L.

ALCOHOL (al′ kə hol′) Alcohol in its most common form is a clear, colorless liquid. It burns and evaporates easily. It has a burning taste. Alcohols are made from chemicals found in living things. They all have hydroxyl (OH) groups which are connected to carbon atoms.

The simplest alcohol is methanol, or methyl alcohol. This poisonous substance is commonly called wood alcohol. It is obtained from the destructive distillation of wood. Its molecules consist of a methyl group (CH_3) connected to a hydroxyl group (OH). Its formula is CH_3OH. Ethanol, or ethyl alcohol, is commonly called grain alcohol. Its formula is C_2H_5OH.

Ethyl alcohol is used for alcoholic beverages, such as beer, wine, and spirits. It is also used as a fuel, as a medical cleanser, as a thinner for shellac or certain resin plastics, and as a source of other chemicals. Methyl

These massive brewery kettles are used to produce ethyl alcohol by fermentation of sugar and starch.

alcohol is used as a fuel. It is also used in combination with other chemicals. Isopropyl alcohol is used in antifreeze, in the making of cosmetics, and as an antiseptic in body rubs. Glycol is used as an antifreeze in automobiles. Butyl alcohol is a varnish or a lacquer. Glycerol, or glycerin, is a softener or preservative used in foods and in inks. It is also used to make nitroglycerin, a substance used in the making of dynamite. J.J.A./J.M.

ALCOHOLISM (al′ kə hȯ′ liz əm) Alcoholism is a disease having to do with the overuse of alcoholic drinks. Such drinks include whiskey, gin, rum, vodka, bourbon, wine, and beer.

Some people can drink alcoholic beverages without serious harm. Other people become addicted to them. These people are called alcoholics. They depend on alcohol to help them ignore problems they cannot solve. They use alcohol in order to relax. If they do not have alcohol regularly, they may feel weak and tired. They may shake and perspire freely. Sometimes they vomit, run a fever, or hallucinate, seeing things that do not exist outside the mind. There are more than ten million alcoholics in the United States. Alcoholism is one of the major diseases in the country.

Alcohol acts as a depressant. A depressant dulls the parts of the brain that control speech, the emotions, judgment, and bodily movement. Because alcohol can blur the vision and slow the reflexes, people who have been drinking should not drive a car. The National Safety Council tells us that about half of the drivers involved in accidents where people are killed have been drinking.

One organization that has been set up to help alcoholics is called Alcoholics Anonymous, or A.A. People at an A.A. meeting discuss their drinking problems with each other. They give each other support in trying to overcome the disease. Sometimes, a drug such as Antabuse is used to help a person stop drinking. Antabuse reacts to alcohol in such a way that a person taking a drink with alcohol in it feels very uncomfortable. That person's discomfort helps him or her to refuse any more alcoholic drinks. *See also* ADDICTION.
J.J.A./J.J.F.

ALDEHYDE (al′ de hīd′) An aldehyde is an organic chemical compound made from alcohol. Its molecules usually contain a hydrocarbon group and one or more aldehyde ($-CHO$) groups. Formaldehyde, HCHO, is one of the most common aldehydes. It does not contain a hydrocarbon group. It is a pungent gas, used mostly as a solution in water. It is called formalin in this form. Formaldehyde is used as a preservative. Also, it is used as a disinfectant and in the making of plastics. Another aldehyde in wide use is acetaldehyde (CH_3CHO). Acetaldehyde is sometimes called ethanal. It is used to make acetic acid and other compounds. W.R.P./J.M.

ALDER (ȯl′ dər) Alders are trees or bushes belonging to the birch family Betulaceae. They have oval, toothed leaves. Most alders are found in the northern hemisphere, but a few species grow in South America. The best-known species is the black alder of Europe.

The wood of the alder, which is soft, is used in making furniture. Alders commonly grow along stream banks. They are valuable in preventing erosion and for providing food and cover for wildlife. *See also* BIRCH FAMILY. S.R.G./M.H.S.

ALEWIFE (āl′ wīf′) The alewife is a silvery fish belonging to the herring family Clupeidae. It is 25 to 30 cm [10 to 12 in] long and has a thin, deep body. Its tail is deeply forked. The alewife is found along the east coast of North America, from Florida to Quebec. The fish is usually anadromous. This means that it lives its adult life in the oceans but returns to freshwater rivers to spawn, or lay its eggs. Many die after this spawning.

Alewives are caught in nets and are used as bait, fertilizer, and pet food. They are occasionally salted, pickled, or smoked to be eaten by man.

When canals were built connecting the Great Lakes with the St. Lawrence and Hudson Rivers, alewives entered the Great Lakes. In the 1960s, there were many alewives unable to swim to the sea. They became a nuisance and a health problem. Landlocked alewives do not grow as large as anadromous alewives. S.R.G./E.C.M.

ALFALFA (al fal′ fə) Alfalfa, also known as lucerne, is a plant which is a member of Leguminosae, the pea family. It grows from 0.6 to 2.1 m [2 to 7 ft] tall and has purple flowers. Like other legumes, alfalfa is able to absorb nitrogen from the air and put it into the soil. It is able to do this because of a bacterium that grows on its roots. Called nitrogen-fixing, this process is important because nitrogen is a valuable plant nutrient that is quickly taken from the soil by other crops. Farmers plant alfalfa in fields to restore nitrogen to the soil.

Alfalfa contains many vitamins. It is an excellent food for animals. It grows fast and tolerates heat, cold, and drought. Alfalfa originally came from Asia but is now planted around the world. *See also* NITROGEN CYCLE. S.R.G./F.W.S.

ALGAE (al′ jē) Algae are the simplest kinds of plants. Algae belong to many divisions. They are divided according to their color. (*See* PLANT KINGDOM.) The accompanying table shows the major algae divisions. Although many of the algae are simple, one-celled plants, others have primitive roots and many cells. They may grow 60 m [200 ft] long. Algae produce food by photosynthesis. They can reproduce in several ways. The one-celled algae usually split into two identical cells. (*See* REPRODUCTION.)

Most algae live in the water of oceans, rivers, and ponds. Some can live in moist places on land. Algae are found on the ice in polar regions. Some are found in the hot springs at Yellowstone National Park, which are nearly 88°C [187°F]. The best-known types of algae are probably the seaweed found at beaches.

Algae are important because they are the start of a food chain that provides food for every animal. Fish depend on algae for their food. People eat the fish. People also use algae. Many people, especially in the Orient, eat certain kinds of algae like dulse, nori, and Irish moss. In addition, we use things produced from algae in many foods such as ice cream, chocolate milk, gelatin, and beer. Algae can be harmful to people when they are present in great numbers. Several species of red dinoflagellates produce a poison which can paralyze a person. When a clam eats the algae, it collects this poison in its tissues. If a person then eats the clam, he or she will be poisoned. The red algae sometimes grow in large colonies. These colonies turn the water red. This is called a red tide. *See also* DIATOMS. S.R.G./M.H.S.

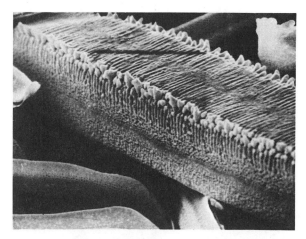

A diatom magnified 3,000 times with a scanning electron microscope. The alga shown is built like a box with a lid. The stripe along the side indicates where the "box" and "lid" come together in the hard glasslike shell. Diatoms occur in various other shapes. They are found in fresh water and seawater.

THE MAIN GROUPS OF ALGAE AND WHERE THEY ARE FOUND.

GREEN ALGAE
(Chlorophyta)

are a varied group which commonly cause scums on ponds. Nearly all the alga forms occur. The examples shown include a single-cell, *Pleurococcus*, which grows on tree trunks; a filament, *Spirogyra*, which is freshwater; and a multicelled flat sheet, *Ulva*, which is a seashore alga, a few inches long. Most green algae are freshwater and microscopic.

EUGLENOIDS
(Euglenophyta)

are single-called forms only. They have a "tinsel" flagellum, rooted in a front pocket, and lack a cell wall, which distinguishes them from green algae. All are microscopic, very common in lakes, rivers, and ponds.

YELLOW-GREEN ALGAE
(Xanthophyta)

do not store starch in their cells, which mainly distinguishes them from green algae. Single-celled and tube forms occur, mostly microscopic and freshwater.

BLUE-GREEN ALGAE
(Cyanophyta)

are more closely related to the bacteria than to other algae. There are single-celled, and filament forms, all microscopic, but they can be seen as "blooms" on lakes. They have no flagella but some can move about slowly. They are mostly freshwater.

Ulva

Pleurococcus grows on tree trunks

Ophiocytium

Nostoc

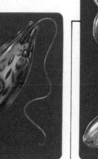

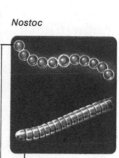

Spirogyra

Euglena

Vaucheria

Oscillatoria

Fresh Water

Sea

Heterosiphonia

Laminaria

Peridinium

Coccosphaera

Eucampia

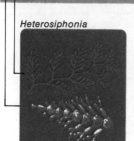

Corallina

Phaeocystis

Fucus

Ceratium

Often a foot or more in length, most red algae are many-celled and of branched or blade shape. Their sex cells, unlike those of the brown algae, have no flagella. They have a pigment which allows growth at deeper levels than other algae. Most live in the sea.

(Rhodophyta)
RED SEAWEEDS

These include the largest algae—some are over 200 ft [60 m] long. Adult plants are made up of millions of cells, but the sex cells are microscopic and flagellated, like the adult cells of some other algae. Most are marine.

(Phaeophyta)
BROWN SEAWEEDS

These often cause phosphorescence in seawater. All are microscopic, with two flagella, single-celled or colonial. Mostly marine.

(Pyrrophyta)
DINOFLAGELLATES

A rather mixed group of microscopic, very delicate algae, some of which form silica cysts. Single-celled, colonial and filament forms are found, in plankton and in cold freshwater. The very tiny Coccolithophores are marine algae covered in round chalky plates. Many chalk cliffs are made up from their bodies.

(Chrysophyta)
GOLDEN ALGAE

Coscinodiscus

Diatoms have hard, sculptured cell walls containing silica. All are microscopic, single-celled or colonial. They have no flagella but can move about slowly. They are common in the sea and in freshwater.

(Bacillariophyta)
DIATOMS

ALGEBRA

Algebra (al′ jə brə) is a branch of mathematics that uses symbols such as letters to stand for numbers, sets of numbers, and values of many kinds. Algebra uses equations and inequalities in solving problems. It also uses negative and imaginary numbers. The word algebra comes from the Arabic word *al-jebr*. The Arab mathematician al-Khowarizmi named one of his books *Al-jebr* in the ninth century. The word referred to topics dealing with equations.

One of the rules in arithmetic is $2 + 3 = 3 + 2$. A general statement taken from this example is that when any two numbers are added together in any order, the answer is the same. This same statement in algebra could be written $x + y = y + x$. The letters x and y stand for any two numbers.

For addition and subtraction in algebra, the common signs, $+$ and $-$, are used. To show that one number is to be multiplied by another, the sign $\times$ is used, or the two numbers or symbols are written next to each other. Sometimes a dot is written between the numbers or symbols. $2x$ means 2 multiplied by x (or x multiplied by 2). A simple way of showing x multiplied by x is to use an exponent. For example, xx is written as x^2. The number ^{2} above and to the right of the x is called the exponent. Exponents are used to show that a number is multiplied by itself many times. 5^6 means $5 \times 5 \times 5 \times 5 \times 5 \times 5$.

Using the above rules, symbols can be combined to form algebraic expressions. The expression $x^2 + 3x - 5$ may have different values, depending on the value of x. If x equals 2, this algebraic expression can be simplified.

$$2^2 + (3 \times 2) - 5$$

$$2^2 = 2 \times 2 = 4 \qquad 3 \times 2 = 6$$

$$4 + 6 - 5$$

Therefore, the expression means $4 + 6 - 5$ and the answer is 5. It makes no difference if the 4 is added to 6 before or after subtracting 5. The calculation may be $10 - 5$ or $4 + 1$. The answer is still 5.

The symbol $=$ means "is equal to," as in $4 = 4$. Problems that use the "equals" sign are called equations. The symbol $\neq$ means "is not equal to," as in $4 \neq 5$. The symbol $<$ means "is less than." For example, $4 < 7$. The symbol $>$ means "is greater than." For example, $7 > 4$. Problems that use these signs are called inequalities.

Algebraic expressions are used to solve many kinds of problems. For example, the statement "the sum of two numbers is ten" may be written $x + y = 10$. The letters x and y stand for any two numbers.

Once you have an equation, the next step is to find out when it is true. An equation is usually true only for certain values of the unknown quantity. For example, the equation $2x = 10$ is only a true statement if $x = 5$. The value of x for which the statement is true is called the solution of the equation.

To find the solutions of some equations, the equation should be thought of as a balance. Whatever is done to one side of the equation must be done to the other side. To solve the equation $2x + 3 = 7$, the diagram shows the $2x + 3$ in the left-hand pan balanced by the 7 in the right-hand pan.

Subtracting 3 from both sides of the equation, the equation becomes $2x = 4$. The pans still balance.

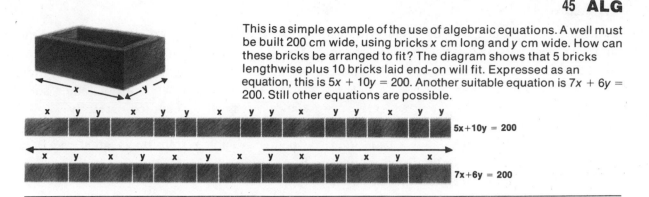

This is a simple example of the use of algebraic equations. A well must be built 200 cm wide, using bricks x cm long and y cm wide. How can these bricks be arranged to fit? The diagram shows that 5 bricks lengthwise plus 10 bricks laid end-on will fit. Expressed as an equation, this is $5x + 10y = 200$. Another suitable equation is $7x + 6y = 200$. Still other equations are possible.

Dividing both sides of the equation by 2, the equation becomes $x = 2$. The solution of the equation is $x = 2$.

More difficult problems are written as equations with two unknown quantities. For instance, an equation might need two numbers that add up to 10. If the two numbers are written as x and y, we can write the expression as $x + y = 10$. If $x = y$, then there is only one solution: x and y must each equal 5. If $x \neq y$, solutions for $x + y = 10$ could be $x = 1, y = 9$; or $x = 2, y = 8$; or $x = 3, y = 7$. This type of equation is called indeterminate.

Another equation might be $x - y = 2$. This equation has many possible solutions, such as $x = 4, y = 2$; or $x = 7, y = 5$; and so on. If the equations $x + y = 10$ and $x - y = 2$ are put together, there is only one set of values of x and y that can satisfy them. The solution is $x = 6$ and $y = 4$.

Using a graph is one way to find the solution. The values of x are shown on the numbered line going from left to right across the page. This is called the x-axis. The values of y go up and down on the other numbered line. This is the y-axis. Some of the solutions of the equation $x + y = 10$ are

$$x = 0, y = 10$$
$$x = 2, y = 8$$
$$x = 4, y = 6.$$

These solutions are marked by the points in red. For example, the point showing the solution $x = 2, y = 8$, is found by moving 2 units across the x-axis and 8 units up the y-axis.

Some solutions of the equation $x - y = 2$ are:

$$x = 10, y = 8$$
$$x = 8, y = 6$$
$$x = 6, y = 4.$$

These solutions are marked by the green points. By connecting the two sets of points, you get two straight lines. These lines are the graphs of the two equations. The point at which the lines cross marks the solution of both equations $x + y = 10$, and $x - y = 2$.

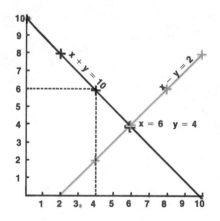

An identity is a statement that is true for any number taking the place of the letter. For example, $a \times (b + c) = (a \times b) + (a \times c)$ is an identity. Another example is $(a + b)^2 = a^2 + 2ab + b^2$.

Mathematics includes many different kinds of algebra to solve problems. Algebra experts are concerned with different symbols and the rules for using them. Algebra has been used to solve problems in chemistry, physics, and engineering.   J.J.A./S.P.A.

ALIMENTARY CANAL (al′ ə ment′ ə rē kə nal′) The alimentary canal is also called the digestive or gastrointestinal tract. It is a long tube within the body of an animal. It usually begins at the mouth and ends at the anus. Some simple animals, such as the Cnidarians, have only one opening.

Food passes through the alimentary canal to be digested and absorbed into the body tissues. Undigested food and wastes are expelled through the anus.   S.R.B./J.J.F.

ALIPHATIC *See* AROMATIC AND ALIPHATIC COMPOUNDS.

ALKALI (al′ kə lī′) An alkali is a base that dissolves easily in water. A solution of a strong alkali has a soapy feeling and a bitter taste. The solution can corrode other substances. It must be handled carefully.

Using an indicator is one way of telling whether or not a solution is alkaline. Red litmus paper will turn blue in an alkali solution.

If an acid and an alkali are mixed in water, a salt is formed. When dry, solid acids and dry

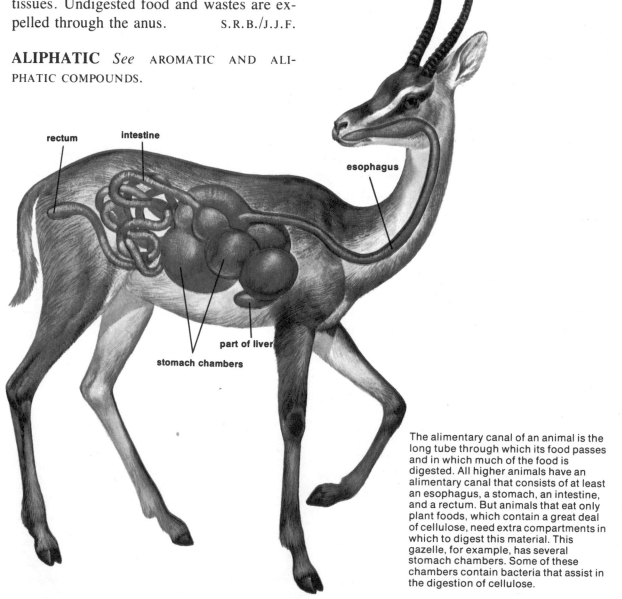

rectum   intestine

esophagus

part of liver

stomach chambers

The alimentary canal of an animal is the long tube through which its food passes and in which much of the food is digested. All higher animals have an alimentary canal that consists of at least an esophagus, a stomach, an intestine, and a rectum. But animals that eat only plant foods, which contain a great deal of cellulose, need extra compartments in which to digest this material. This gazelle, for example, has several stomach chambers. Some of these chambers contain bacteria that assist in the digestion of cellulose.

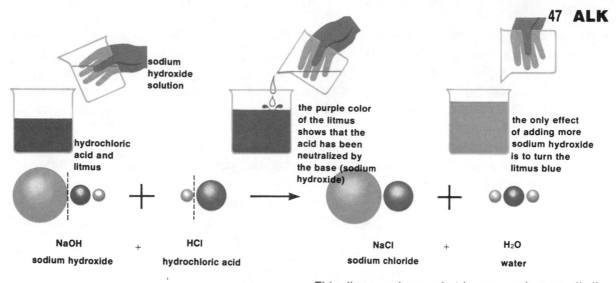

NaOH
sodium hydroxide

+

HCl
hydrochloric acid

NaCl
sodium chloride

+

H₂O
water

sodium hydroxide solution

hydrochloric acid and litmus

the purple color of the litmus shows that the acid has been neutralized by the base (sodium hydroxide)

the only effect of adding more sodium hydroxide is to turn the litmus blue

This diagram shows what happens when an alkali and acid interact chemically. Sodium hydroxide is a strong alkali. When a water solution of sodium hydroxide is mixed with hydrochloric acid, a neutral salt, sodium chloride, is formed. The litmus indicator is red in acid and blue in alkali.

alkalis are mixed, no neutralizing chemical change occurs. Ordinary baking powder is a mixture of dry acid and dry, alkaline salt.

Strong alkalis are used as cleaning substances. They are also used in the making of soap. The best known strong alkalis are sodium hydroxide (NaOH), also called caustic soda, and potassium hydroxide (KOH), known as caustic potash. Potassium hydroxide is used mainly in the making of soap and in medicine. Sodium hydroxide is used in the manufacture of other chemicals, rayon, film, and soap. It is also used in medicine.

J.J.A./A.D.

ALKALI METAL (al′ kə lī′ met′ əl) The alkali metals are a group of six elements which make up group IA of the periodic table. (See ELEMENT.) The elements are lithium (Li), sodium (Na), potassium (K), rubidium (Rb), cesium (Cs), and francium (Fr). These metals are not found in nature. They are found only as ions in different chemicals.

Each of the alkali metals has a silvery shine. Each is a good conductor of electricity and heat. Each is easily molded or shaped. These metals are soft. They can be cut with a knife.

The alkali metals are difficult to handle and store because of their chemical reactivity. They are often stored under kerosene or some other liquid. They react violently with water,

giving off hydrogen and forming bases. All the alkali metals have a valence of one. This means that they gain or share one electron in bonding with other atoms. See also BOND (CHEMICAL).

J.J.A./A.D.

ALKALINE EARTH METAL (al′ kə·lən ərth′ met′ əl) The alkaline earth metals are a group of six elements which make up Group IIA of the periodic table. (See ELEMENT.) These elements are beryllium (Be), magnesium (Mg), calcium (CA), strontium (Sr), barium (Ba), and radium (Ra). They are usually found in the ground. The alkaline earth metals are harder and have higher melting points and boiling points than the alkali metals have.

The alkaline earth metals react with water, giving off hydrogen gas and forming bases. They do not react as rapidly as the alkali metals.

All the alkaline earth metals gain or share two electrons in bonding with other atoms, giving them a valence of two. See also BOND (CHEMICAL).

J.J.A./A.D.

ALKALOID (al′ kə loid′) An alkaloid is an organic compound containing nitrogen

(N). Alkaloids are made by plants as waste products. They serve no useful purpose for the plants. Alkaloids are solids which appear as crystals, except for coniine, found in hemlock, and nicotine, found in tobacco. Both of these alkaloids are liquids. Alkaloids dissolve in alcohol, but not in water. Alkaloids often have harsh effects on humans and animals. They combine with acids. We get them in this form from crushed plants.

Some alkaloids, like coniine, are deadly poisons. Strychnine, which comes from various trees, causes muscles to shake and tighten. Curare, a mixture of alkaloids, also comes from trees. Curare was first used by natives in South America. They dipped their arrowheads in it so that animals died when wounded. Also known as arrow poison, curare relaxes muscles. It is sometimes used in surgery for this purpose.

Alkaloids have been used to kill insects. Small doses of belladonna were once used by women to improve their beauty. The drug makes the pupils of the eyes larger. Morphine, from the opium poppy, and cocaine, from the coca plant, were once widely used as anesthetics. They are now seldom used for this purpose because they are addictive. Quinine, from the bark of cinchona, was used to fight the disease malaria. Caffeine is an alkaloid in coffee and tea. Theobromine occurs in cocoa. J.J.A./J.M.

ALLERGY (al′ ər jē) An allergy is an abnormal sensitivity of the body to certain substances. These substances are normally harmless. Some things to which a person may be allergic are feathers, dust, pollen from plants, certain foods, some medicines, and bee stings. Such substances are called allergens. One person may be allergic to feathers but another person may not be. Feathers are an allergen only to the first person. When a person comes near an allergen, he may react by sneezing, coughing, or even vomiting. He may break out in a rash or hives, which are spots of fluid in the skin. Some allergic reactions last for a few hours. Some last several days. Several common disorders, partly or wholly caused by allergens, are bronchial asthma, eczema, and hay fever. These allergies may be inherited.

The body produces a large number of antibodies which attack and destroy any "foreign" material in the bloodstream. People who are allergic to feathers have an antibody in their blood which attacks feather particles. The response of the body to the "battle" between the particle and the antibody is the allergic reaction. Drugs called antihistamines help lessen allergic reactions.

Some people have antibodies that react to penicillin, a drug which is helpful to most people. The reaction to a shot of penicillin may be fatal to a person with an allergy to it. Such a reaction is called anaphylactic shock. S.R.G./J.J.F.

ALLIGATOR (al′ ə gāt′ ər) Alligators are reptiles that belong to the Alligatoridae family. There are seven species of alligators and the smaller caimans. The largest species is the American alligator which grows to 5.7 m [19 ft] long. It is found only in the southeastern United States. A smaller species, the Chinese alligator, grows to 1.8 m [6 ft] long and is found along the Yangtse River. All species live in warm climates and can swim.

Alligators live near water where they eat fish, frogs, birds, and other animals. Very large adults can eat a deer, or, very rarely, a human. Alligators have large mouths and many sharp teeth. They make nests at the edge of water and lay 20 to 50 eggs during the summer.

Alligators are very similar to crocodiles. Crocodiles have pointed noses, however. Alligators have blunt noses. S.R.G./C.J.C.

ALLOTROPE (al′ ə trōp′) An allotrope is a physical form of an element that is different from the element's original form. Many elements can exist in more than one physical form. Allotropes result from the way single atoms or groups of atoms are arranged. Carbon is an element that has many allotropes. It can appear as a soft, black substance called graphite. Another form, called diamond, is very hard and crystalline in appearance.

Phosphorus has several allotropes. Yellow phosphorus and red phosphorus are the best known. Yellow phosphorus burns at room temperature 20°C [68°F]. It is poisonous and luminous. Red phosphorus does not burn at room temperature. It is neither poisonous nor luminous. Sulfur is another allotropic element. It exists as rhombic sulfur below 96°C [204.8°F]. Above that temperature, it changes into monoclinic sulfur. Tin and oxygen are other elements that exhibit allotropy. W.R.P./A.D.

ALLOY (al′ oi′) An alloy is a mixture of two or more metals. The metals are combined by heating them until they become liquid. An alloy is made when the metals remain evenly mixed after cooling and becoming solid.

Metals in their pure form are often too weak for most uses. They can be improved by mixing one or more other metals with them to form alloys. Pure aluminum is light, but weak. When copper and magnesium are added to it, the aluminum becomes stronger. Copper and tin are soft and weak. Mixed together in an alloy, they form the harder, stronger bronze. Brass, a mixture of copper and zinc, is another strong and useful alloy. Copper is often used in making alloys. It is used in cupronickel from which some coins are made.

Alloys can also be made by adding a non-metal, like carbon or silicon, to a metal. Steel is made of carbon, iron, and traces of other metals. Iron by itself is very weak and soft compared to steel. Only a small amount of carbon is needed to make the change to steel. Ordinary steel contains less than .25% carbon.

Alloys do more than just make a metal harder and stronger. Each type of element mixed has a certain effect on the total mass of metal. If chromium, nickel, and molybdenum are added to steel, the rust-free alloy called stainless steel is produced. Stainless steel, also stronger than ordinary steel, is only one of many alloy steels used in industry.

Most metals dissolve in one another in

A special alloy was used to make this large ship's propeller. Manganese bronze resists corrosion.

SOME IMPORTANT ALLOYS

Ferrous alloys (mainly iron)	Major Properties	Major Uses	Typical amounts of elements other than iron
High-alloy steels and stainless steels	Very hard, strong steels, often resistant to corrosion.	Used for tools to cut, drill, and draw other metals, and for high-strength metal parts. Stainless steels are often used for cutlery.	0.1–2.0% carbon, up to 27% chromium or 20% tungsten or 15% nickel, and lesser amounts of vanadium, cobalt, molybdenum, zirconium, or tantalum.
Mild steels	Hard, strong, workable steels, more resistant to corrosion than pure iron.	Used for most steel constructions other than those above. Widely used for automobiles and ships.	0.1–1.5% carbon, very small amounts of other elements.
Cast iron	Hard but brittle.	Used widely in early industrial times.	2–3% carbon, a few per cent silicon and other elements.

Nonferrous alloys (little or no iron)	Major Properties	Major Uses	Typical amounts of elements
Aluminum alloys	Fairly hard, strong, very light alloys, often with good corrosion resistance and good electrical conductivity.	Used widely where lightness plus strength is required. Applications include tubes for boilers, automobile bodies, buildings, food equipment, foil, kitchenware, electric cables.	85–95% aluminum, with small amounts of chromium, copper, manganese or silicon, and up to 4% magnesium.
Aluminum bronze	Tough, but workable, and resistant to corrosion by seawater.	Nuts, bolts, ships' tubes and sheets.	77.5% copper, 2% aluminum, 20.5% zinc.
Manganese bronze	Very good resistance to wear.	Automobile clutch disks, valves, and pumps.	58.5% copper, 39% zinc, 1.5% iron, 1.0% tin.
Phosphor bronze	Strong, fairly corrosion-resistant, good electrical conductivity.	Chemical equipment, electric motor brushes.	95% copper, 5% tin.
Bronze	Resistant to corrosion by seawater	Superstructure and other parts on ships.	90% copper, 10% zinc.
Naval brass	Fairly strong and workable. Attractive yellow color.	Portholes and other parts on ships.	60% copper, 39% zinc, 1% tin.
Red brass	Workable, fairly resistant to corrosion.	Plumbing for houses (but plastics often replace it).	85% copper, 15% zinc.
Copper-nickel alloys	Hard, heat- and corrosion-resistant.	Chemical equipment.	69–88.5% copper, 10–30% nickel, some iron and manganese.
Nickel-copper alloys	Hard, resistant to many acids and alkalis.	Chemical equipment.	About 31% copper, 64% nickel, small amounts of carbon, iron, manganese, and silicon.
Nickel-chromium alloys	Very resistant to heat. Good resistance to corrosion.	Airplane exhausts, food and dairy equipment.	About 68% nickel, 15% chromium, 9% iron, small amounts of carbon, copper, manganese, silicon, and tellurium.
Nickel-molybdenum alloys	Extremely good heat-resistance. Good resistance to corrosion.	Jet airplane engines, missiles, furnaces.	About 55% nickel, 30% molybdenum, 5% zinc, 4% iron, 2.5% copper, some carbon, chromium, manganese, silicon, and silver.
Lead alloys	Soft, but antimony lead is harder. Good acid resistance (not oxidizing acids).	House roofs and acid equipment. Antimony lead is used for storage battery grids.	94–99.7% lead, up to 6% antimony.
Pewter	Attractive shiny gray colour.	Drinking mugs and ornamental objects.	91% lead, 7% antimony, 2% copper.
White metal	A fairly soft alloy.	Bearings for motors.	92% tin, 8% antimony.
Magnesium alloys	Very light, fairly hard. Not very resistant to corrosion.	Small parts for engines, where lightness in weight is very important.	About 90% magnesium, 7% aluminum, 1.5% zinc, and a little manganese.
Titanium alloys* *Although used only recently, titanium is the ninth commonest element in the Earth's crust.	Lightweight, very strong, resistant to corrosion.	Jet airplane, missile, and ships' engines, and chemical equipment.	Mostly titanium, with up to 13% vanadium, 11% chromium, 8% manganese, 6% aluminum, and some other metals.
Noble metal alloys	Generally rather soft and workable. Resist corrosion (tarnish) well. Often very heat resistant.	Expensive alloys used in jewelry. Harder types, such as osmiridium, are used to tip fountain pen nibs.	Alloys containing platinum, rhodium, osmium, iridium, ruthenium, palladium, gold, or silver.

certain proportions. Copper and nickel can mix together, no matter how much of either element is used. They are said to be totally miscible. A few pairs of metals, such as lead and aluminum, are immiscible. They cannot be mixed together at all.

Alloys usually have cooling rates different from those of pure metals. Pure metals turn solid at a specific temperature. Above that temperatue, they are liquid. Below it, they are solid. Most alloys have a range. This means an alloy may turn solid anywhere between many degrees of temperature. An equal mixture of the copper-nickel alloy, for instance, has a range from 1,312°C [2,394°F] to 1,248°C [2,278°F].

A few alloys behave like pure metals, melting at certain temperatures. In all these alloys, the amount of each metal used is such that the lowest possible melting point is obtained. Wood's metal is one example. An alloy of bismuth, lead, tin, and cadmium, it melts at 70°C [158°F]. It is used in valves of sprinkler systems in public buildings. There, if a fire starts, its heat melts the Wood's metal seal. This releases the water to put out the fire. Such alloys and their melting temperatures, are called eutectic.

Alloys have many uses. Tungsten increases resistance to scraping. Vanadium and aluminum give metal a hard but smooth structure. Phosphorus makes low-carbon steel stronger and easier to work. Lead alloy is used most often in the making of electrodes in storage batteries. Zinc alloys, used in nickel and chrome plating, are used in the making of automobiles.   J.J.A./A.D.

ALLUVIUM (ə lü′ vē əm). Alluvium is gravel, sand, silt, or mud which has been deposited by water. Alluvium is found at the banks and mouths of rivers or alongside lakes and oceans. It is also found where rivers, lakes, or oceans once existed but have since dried up.

Erosion washes soil into streams. The streams carry the soil downstream. When the speed of the water slows, the water cannot carry the heavier objects that are in it. These objects are dropped and left behind. Also, when a stream enters a larger stream or body of water such as a lake, it will drop its load of sediment or mud. Gravel is deposited first because it is the heaviest. Deltas are alluvial deposits usually consisting of silts and clays. Silt and clay are light. They remain suspended in the water until the stream that carries them reaches the mouth of the river. Alluvial plains are found in flat valleys where the river has flooded and deposited mud. Alluvial plains are among the most fertile and densely populated regions in the world.   S.R.G./W.R.S.

ALMOND (äm′ ənd) The almond tree belongs to the rose family Rosaceae. Its nutlike fruit is called an almond. The almond is not really a nut. It is a hard seed from a fleshy fruit, similar to a peach. The tree is small, only growing to 6 m [20 ft]. It is very attractive. It resembles the peach tree, to which it is related. The almond tree is originally from southwest Asia. It now grows in warm climates around the world. In the United States, almonds are grown in California.

There are two types of almonds. One is bitter, and one is sweet. The sweet almond is eaten and used in foods. The bitter almond contains small amounts of the deadly poison, hydrocyanic acid.   S.R.G./F.W.S.

ALOE (al′ ō) The aloes are a group of succulent plants belonging to the lily family, Liliaceae. They grow rosettes, which are spiral-shaped bunches of fleshy leaves. A tall spike of flowers grows up from the center. Aloes are found in the dry regions of Africa and Asia. They are similar to the agaves of the Americas. Aloes are grown for decoration and are used in medicine.   S.R.G./M.H.S.

ALPHA CENTAURI (al′ fə sen tȯr′ ē) Alpha Centauri is the name of the star system that is closest to earth. It is also the third brightest star in the sky. Alpha Centauri is a member of the constellation Centaurus. This constellation is the southern hemisphere of the sky. Alpha Centauri is about 4.3 light-years away from earth. Traveling at the speed of light (297,920 km/sec or 186,200 mi/sec), it would take an object four years and three months to get there. Scientists once believed that Alpha Centauri was a single star. It is now known that it is a triple star. One of its stars, Proxima Centauri, is the nearest star to our sun. *See also* ASTRONOMY; CONSTELLATION; SOUTHERN CROSS.   G.M.B./C.R.

ALPHA PARTICLE (al′ fə pärt′ i kəl) Alpha particles are positively charged particles given off by certain radioactive materials. (*See* RADIOACTIVITY.) They are made up of two neutrons and two protons bound together. Alpha particles are identical to the nuclei of helium-4 atoms. They were discovered by Ernest Rutherford, in 1899.

Radioactive elements like uranium and radium give off alpha and beta particles and gamma rays. When their nuclei decay, alpha particles are the least dangerous of the three. They can be stopped by a piece of paper or by a few centimeters of air. Alpha particles are not harmful to man unless they actually enter the body.

Alpha particles can be detected by a Geiger counter. They will also leave tracks on a photographic film or make a flash of light on a fluorescent screen. *See also* BETA PARTICLES; GAMMA RAYS.   W.R.P./J.T.

ALTERNATING CURRENT (ôl′ tər nāt′ ing kər′ ənt) An alternating current is an electrical current that changes direction regularly. It can be produced by an electrical generator. A generator has a coil of wire spinning between the poles of a magnet. The magnet causes a current to flow in the coil as it spins. The direction of the current changes twice in every spin. During the first quarter of the spin,

it builds up to a maximum in one direction. Then it goes back to zero at the end of half of the spin. At this point, the current changes direction. It then builds up to a maximum in the other direction and reduces to zero after it has completed the spin. This is called a cycle and usually there is a complete cycle every fraction of a second. When the coil spins round once, the current goes through one complete cycle. At the end of the cycle, the current changes direction to start a new cycle. This is the most common way of producing an alternating current. Another way is to spin the magnet around inside the coil of wire. (*See* ELECTROMAGNETISM.)   M.E./J.T.

ALTERNATION OF GENERATIONS (ôl′ tər nā′ shən uv jen′ ə rā′ shənz) Alternation of generations is the alternation of two distinct stages in an organism's life cycle. It is characteristic of some lower animals, such as some members of the phyla Protozoa, Platyhelminthes, and Cnidaria, and many plants, including some seed plants as well as most lower plants—algae, fungi, mosses, and ferns.

In alternation of generations, the gametophyte (gamete-producing) generation alternates with the sporophyte (spore-producing) generation. The gametophyte, or haploid, generation is the sexually reproductive stage in an organism's life cycle. It produces male gametes (sperm) and female gametes (eggs) which combine to form a zygote. (*See* GAMETE.) The zygote develops into a new organism, the sporophyte. The sporophyte, or diploid, generation is the asexually reproductive stage in an organism's life cycle. The sporophyte produces spores, which develop into new organisms. (*See* SPORE.)

Although alternation of generations is common in many organisms, one of the two stages may be difficult to observe. This may be due to the fact that it may be very small or short-lived. Frequently, one generation looks totally different from the other generation, even though the same species is involved. *See also* ASEXUAL REPRODUCTION; REPRODUCTION. A.J.C./E.R.L.

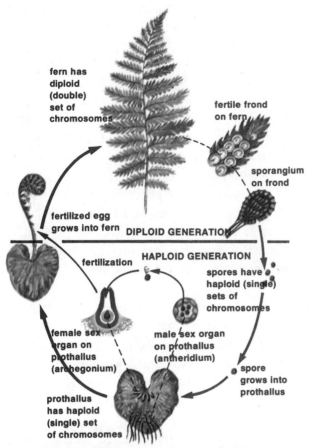

Alternation of generations is shown clearly by a fern. The fern plant (top) is the diploid generation, having a double set of chromosomes. The smaller prothallus plant (bottom) is the haploid generation, having a single set of chromosomes.

fern has diploid (double) set of chromosomes

fertile frond on fern

sporangium on frond

fertilized egg grows into fern **DIPLOID GENERATION**

HAPLOID GENERATION

fertilization

spores have haploid (single) sets of chromosomes

female sex organ on prothallus (archegonium)

male sex organ on prothallus (antheridium)

spore grows into prothallus

prothallus has haploid (single) set of chromosomes

ALTIMETER (al tim′ ət ər) An altimeter is an instrument in an airplane that shows how high the plane is above the earth. The barometric or aneroid altimeter, used in many small planes, shows the height above sea level. It measures the decrease in air pressure as the altitude increases. Since air pressure changes, this type of altimeter must be adjusted to the air pressure on the ground before each flight.

Most large planes carry altimeters that are more accurate than the barometric type. Radio or absolute altimeters bounce electronic signals off the earth's surface, much like radar. The time it takes for the echoes to return is interpreted into a precise measurement of the altitude. The capacitance altimeter indicates altitude by measuring the difference between electrical charges of the earth and plane. The sonic altimeter bounces sound signals off the earth's surface. It times the echoes to determine the altitude. *See also* ATMOSPHERE; BAROMETER. W.R.P./R.W.L.

altimeter readings

2,400 feet

9,100 feet

12,300 feet

An airplane altimeter, showing a typical reading.

ALTITUDE (al′ tə tüd′) Altitude is the height of an object above a surface or horizon. It is measured from the ground or from the surface of the oceans (sea level). Altitude is given as an angle in degrees, minutes, and seconds. The altitude of the sun, moon, stars, and planets is measured from the horizon.

Airplanes carry instruments called altimeters which are sensitive to atmospheric pressure. An altimeter measures in feet or meters the altitudes at which an airplane flies. (*See* BAROMETER.) The altitudes of mountains are called elevations. Mt. Everest, the highest mountain on Earth, has an elevation of 8,848 m [29,028 ft]. Maps show altitudes of land with contour lines. *See also* MAP AND MAPPING. W.R.P./J.VP.

ALUM (al′ əm) An alum is a double sulfate formed with a univalent element or radical.

One common alum is potash alum. Potash alum is a double sulfate of potassium and aluminum. It forms colorful eight-sided crystals. Its chemical formula is $KAl(SO_4)_2 \cdot 12H_2O$. Potash alum is used in dyeing leather, paper, and fabrics. It is used in medicine to stop small cuts from bleeding. Alums are also used to purify water. *See also* VALENCE.   J.J.A./A.D.

ALUMINUM (ə lü′ mə nəm) Aluminum is a silvery white metallic element with the symbol Al. The atomic number of aluminum is 13 and its atomic weight is 26.98. It melts at 660°C [1,220°F] and boils at 2,467°C [4,473°F]. Its relative density is 2.7. Aluminum is a very common metal and makes up 8% of the Earth's crust. It was discovered by Friedrich Wohler, a German chemist in 1827. For many years, it was an expensive metal. Then, in 1886, a cheap way of producing pure aluminum was discovered. It is now a widely used metal.

Extraction   Most aluminum comes from a mineral called bauxite. Bauxite is common in many countries. There are many bauxite deposits in Arkansas. Bauxite contains aluminum oxide, often called alumina. The alumina is obtained from the bauxite by washing and refining. Then it is mixed with cryolite, another mineral that contains aluminum. A powerful electric current is passed through the mixture in an electrolytic cell. (*See* ELECTROLYSIS.) The current generates a temperature of about 1,000°C [1,832°F]. The aluminum melts and falls to the bottom of the cell, where it is collected. This process needs large amounts of electricity. About 10 kilowatt-hours of electricity are needed to make 0.5 kg [1 lb] of aluminum. Because of this, most aluminum is extracted in areas where hydroelectric power is plentiful. This form of power is cheap.

Uses of aluminum   Aluminum is a very light strong metal with many different uses. It is used for making pots and pans because it is a good conductor of heat. Aluminum also conducts electricity well and is used to make electrical wires. It can be pressed into a thin

Aluminum is made from bauxite ore, a natural form of aluminum oxide. The diagram shows the process.

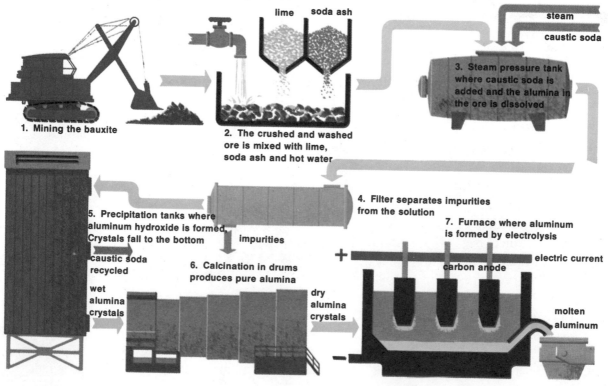

lime   soda ash

steam

caustic soda

1. Mining the bauxite

2. The crushed and washed ore is mixed with lime, soda ash and hot water

3. Steam pressure tank where caustic soda is added and the alumina in the ore is dissolved

4. Filter separates impurities from the solution

5. Precipitation tanks where aluminum hydroxide is formed. Crystals fall to the bottom

caustic soda recycled

impurities

6. Calcination in drums produces pure alumina

7. Furnace where aluminum is formed by electrolysis

electric current

carbon anode

wet alumina crystals

dry alumina crystals

molten aluminum

foil that is used in wrapping foods, candy, and cigarettes.

Because aluminum is light but strong, it is widely used in airplanes and spacecraft. It can be made even stronger by mixing it with other metals to form alloys. Duralumin is such an alloy. It is used as the outer surface of many airplanes. The bodies and parts of some automobiles, trucks, boats, and trains are made from aluminum alloys.

Seawater corrodes aluminum. (*See* CORROSION.) Alloys of aluminum have been developed that do not corrode. Aluminum is not corroded by fresh water nor by the atmosphere. This is because it forms a thin coating of its oxide on its surface. This is called anodizing. It is usually done to finished products like window frames, screen doors, and drainpipes. *See also* ELECTROLYSIS.

M.E./J.R.W.

AM *See* MODULATION.

AMALGAM (ə mal′ gəm) An amalgam is an alloy of a metal with mercury. This alloy is like a solution of the metal in mercury. Mercury is normally a liquid. An amalgam may also be a solid, depending on how much metal is used in relation to the amount of mercury.

Precious metals, like gold or silver, can be dissolved out of their ores with the use of mercury. The gold or silver is then removed from the amalgam by boiling off the mercury.

Amalgams of copper (Cu) and cadmium (Cd) are used as dental cement. Dentists use mercury amalgam for the silver fillings in teeth. J.J.A./A.D.

AMARANTH FAMILY About 500 species of herbaceous, dicotyledon plants make up the amaranth (am′ ə ranth′) family, Amaranthaceae. They are found in warm, temperate

The processing plant above shows large rolls of sheet aluminum. One of the main uses of aluminum is in the production of cans that hold a variety of liquids.

This blaze of color is characteristic of the amaranth family. Shown here is Celosia, or golden plume.

regions. In North America, they grow in the south and southwestern United States. The genus, *Amaranthus*, has about 50 species of annual plants. Some of them are noted for the long life of their green or red flowers. One popular garden plant that belongs to the genus is called love-lies-bleeding.   S.R.G./M.H.S.

AMARYLLIS FAMILY There are more than 700 species of monocotyledons in the amaryllis (am′ ə ril′ əs) family, Amaryllidaceae. They closely resemble members of the lily family. Most amaryllis species are tropical or subtropical. Many grow in dry regions. There are about 40 species in North America, including the daffodil and snowdrop. The succulent, agave, is also a member of the family. Agave grows in the southwestern United States and in Mexico.

S.R.G./M.H.S.

Members of the Amaryllis family from various parts of the world. The narcissus flowers early in temperate climates. The cape lily, kaffir lily, and the agave all come from warm climates, but can be grown in temperate zones. Agave flowers look like candelabras.

narcissus

kafir lily

cape lily

agave

AMBER (am′ bər) Amber is pine tree sap that dripped out of coniferous trees millions of years ago and was buried. During the time it was buried, it hardened into a yellow or brown stone that looks like glass. Sometimes, insects fell into the sticky sap, which is also called resin. They became fossils inside the amber. Amber is now used for many things, including cigarette holders, beads, combs, and umbrella handles.   S.R.G./W.R.S.

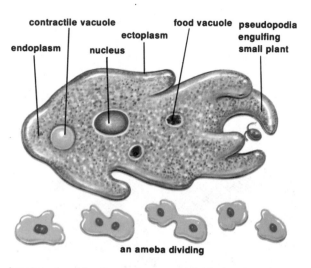

contractile vacuole   food vacuole   pseudopodia engulfing small plant

ectoplasm

endoplasm   nucleus

an ameba dividing

Amebas feed by flowing around their food and then bringing it into their bodies.
Amebas reproduce by simple fission. The nucleus divides, splitting the cell in two.

AMEBA (ə mē′ bə) An ameba is an animal having only one cell. It belongs to the phylum Protozoa. Most amebas can be seen only with a microscope. They live in water or in places that are moist, such as under wet leaves. The ameba is one of the most common animals on earth. Amebas can even be found inside the intestinal tracts of human beings and other animals. Some species of amebas cause disease.

Everything the ameba needs is in its one cell. Its nucleus acts as its control center, and its vacuoles store foods and waste. The ameba's cell is filled with a jellylike substance called cytoplasm, as are the cells in the human body.

An ameba feeds on bacteria. Its soft body wraps around a bacterium and surrounds it. The bacterium is then enclosed in a food vacuole and digested.

The ameba moves by slowly projecting a part of its body forward and letting the rest of its body ooze up to it. The part of the body projected is called a pseudopodium, which means "false foot."

The ameba reproduces by cell division to form two identical cells. (*See* REPRODUCTION.)   S.R.G./C.S.H.

AMERICIUM (am′ ə ris′ ē əm) Americium is a silvery metallic element. Its symbol is Am and its atomic number is 95. Americium has two main isotopes. Their atomic weights are 241 and 243. The metal melts at about 1,000°C [1,832°F] and it boils at 2,607°C [4,725°F]. Its relative density is 13.7. Americium is not found naturally and has to be made artificially. It was first made in 1944 by a team of American scientists led by Glenn T. Seaborg. They made it by bombarding plutonium with neutrons in a nuclear reactor.

Americium is strongly radioactive and is used in research. For example, it is used as a tracer to study the amount of water in the soil. *See also* NEUTRON.   M.E./J.R.W.

AMETHYST (am′ ə thəst) Amethyst is a variety of quartz, found in the form of six-sided, pointed crystals. It is a bluish violet or purple stone. It has a hardness of 7 on the Mohs scale. When heated, amethyst turns to a brilliant yellow or a light brown.

Amethyst is used in jewelry. It is the birthstone for February. The most prized amethysts are transparent, with a deep, even color. The color is caused by iron and manganese oxides. Oriental amethyst, the same bluish violet or purple color as true amethyst, is a form of corundum.   J.J.A./R.H.

AMINE (ə mēn′) An amine is a chemical compound. It is a base which reacts with an acid to form a salt. It is usually formed from ammonia (NH_3). To form amines, the hydrogen atoms in ammonia are replaced with radicals containing carbon atoms. If an amine contains one of these carbon radicals, it is called a primary amine. If it contains two of the radicals, it is called a secondary amine. Most amines have a fishy or musty smell. They are used in making dyes. *See also* ANILINE.   S.R.G./J.M.

AMINO ACID (ə mē′ nō as′ əd) An amino acid is an organic compound possessing both acidic and basic characteristics. Most amino acids have the following general chemical structure:

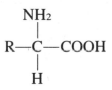

NH_2 is called the "amino group," COOH the carboxyl group, and R represents the rest of the molecule. The differences in "R" make one amino acid different from another.

Amino acids are the building blocks of proteins. (*See* PROTEIN.) Proteins are made of long, complex chains of amino acids. These chains contain as few as four or as many as several hundred amino acids. Most proteins found in plants, animals, and microorganisms are made of different combinations of 22 of these amino acids. Plants and some microorganisms are able to produce all the amino acids they need. Human beings and most higher animals, however, cannot produce all the necessary amino acids. The eight amino acids which are not made by the body are called the "essential amino acids." They must be supplied by food in the diet. (*See* DIET.) The essential amino acids are found in eggs, milk products, meats, and some vegetables.

During digestion, certain types of enzymes called proteases break proteins into amino acids. These amino acids are small enough to be absorbed into the blood. They then travel to the tissues where they are rebuilt into the new proteins which the body needs. Extra amino acids are not built into proteins, but are broken down again and converted into urea. Urea is then excreted as part of urine. (*See* EXCRETION.) *See also* DIGESTION; ENZYME.   A.J.C./E.R.L.

AMMETER (am′ ēt ′ər) The ammeter is an instrument for measuring electric current. The measurement is usually in amperes. There are three main kinds of ammeters.

The moving coil ammeter is like a galvanometer. It has a coil of wire between the poles of a permanent magnet. As electric current passes through the coil, it creates a magnetic field around the coil. The field of the coil and the field of the magnet make the coil move. A needle attached to the coil moves to show the amount the coil has moved. The distance it moves depends on how much current passes through the coil. The moving coil ammeter is designed for direct current, not alternating current. A rectifier is added to the moving coil ammeter if alternating current must be measured.

The moving-iron ammeter has two pieces of iron inside a coil. One of the iron pieces can move. The other piece cannot move. The current passing through the coil produces a magnetic field. The force of the field moves one piece of iron away from the other. A needle on a scale shows how far apart the two pieces of iron move. The moving-iron ammeter can measure direct current or alternating current. It does not need a rectifier.

A hot-wire ammeter measures the heat produced by an electric current passing through it. The electric current heats a wire, causing it to expand. A needle is attached to indicate how much the wire expands.

Ammeters usually can be found wherever electrical power is in use. They are common in automobiles and appliances as well as larger machines that use electricity.

G.M.B./R.W.L.

AMMONIA (ə mō′ nyə) Ammonia is a gas which is a compound of nitrogen and hydrogen. Its chemical formula is NH_3. It has a strong odor. Ammonia can be obtained by distilling coal into coke and coal gas. (*See* DISTILLATION.) Ammonia can also be made by combining hydrogen and nitrogen with a catalyst under pressure at a high temperature. This process is called the Haber process.

The ammonia used as a household cleaner is a strong solution of gas in water. Ammonia has many industrial uses. Since it can be broken down easily into hydrogen and nitrogen, ammonia is used to transport hydrogen. Ammonia was once widely used as a refrigerant, but is now outdated. Smelling salts contain chemicals which release ammonia. The shock of the smell wakes up people who have fainted.

Ammonia is also used to make ammonium compounds. It is used to make nitric acid, and to dissolve certain substances. Salts of ammonia can be made by adding ammonia to an acid. These salts are called ammonium salts. The ammonia takes on a hydrogen atom to form an ammonium radical $(NH_4)^+$. For example, ammonium chloride (NH_4Cl) is

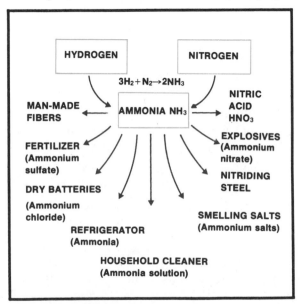

made by mixing ammonia (NH_3) and hydrochloric acid (HCl). The most important ammonium compound is ammonium sulfate. It is made from ammonia (NH_3) and sulfuric acid (H_2SO_4). It is used as a fertilizer because it provides nitrogen for the soil. Ammonium chloride, also called sal ammoniac, is used in the manufacture of dry cells. It is also used in dyeing and printing. Ammonium nitrate is used in fertilizers, explosives, and in making nitrous oxide, sometimes called "laughing gas."   J.J.A./A.D.

AMMONITE (am′ ə nīt′) Ammonites were members of a large group of mollusks that lived 70,000,000 years ago. They are now extinct. They resembled a modern mollusk, the nautilus. Most ammonites had coiled shells, so the group was named after the Egyptian god, Ammon, who had coiled horns. Ammonites are found as fossils in rocks ranging from the Lower Jurassic to Upper Cretaceous in age. *See also* FOSSILS.

S.R.G./W.R.S.

Ammonites are among the most beautiful fossils. They are the remains of extinct mollusks that resembled the present-day nautilus. Some ammonites measured as much as six ft [1.8 m] in diameter.

AMPERE (am′ pir) The ampere, named after the French physicist André Ampère, is the basic unit used to measure the flow of an electric current. Its symbol is A.

One measurement of the ampere may be stated in terms of electromagnetism. Electric current flows at the rate of 1 ampere when 1 coulomb flows past a section of an electric circuit in 1 second. The coulomb is an amount of electricity equal to the charge of 6.24×10^{18} electrons. In other words, 1 ampere equals 1 coulomb per second.

The difference between a coulomb and an ampere lies in the difference between quantity and rate. For instance, a container may hold ten liters of water. This is the container's quantity. A faucet may pour out a liter of water per minute. This is the rate. There is a coulomb, or quantity, of electricity. There is also an ampere, or rate, of electricity.

Electric current is measured with an ammeter. A 100 watt light bulb requires about 1 ampere of current if the voltage is about 100 volts.

Physicists define amperes in terms of the magnetic force, measured in newtons, a current produces. In electrochemistry, the ampere is the standard current depositing silver at the rate of 0.001118 grams per second when passed through a solution of silver nitrate.

Some scientific instruments use currents measured in microamperes, or millionths of amperes. Some large industrial equipment uses current measured in kiloamperes, or thousands of amperes. *See also* OHM; VOLT.

J.J.A./R.W.L.

AMPÈRE, ANDRÉ (1775–1836) André Ampère (an pâ′ r′) was a French physicist and mathematician. In 1814, he was elected to the Academy of Science for his important work in mathematics. Ampère had an even greater interest in electricity. He used his own apartment as a laboratory and made his own tools in order to work on various experiments. Ampère's work was the beginning of the new science of electrodynamics. Electrodynamics is the branch of physics having to do with the way electric currents affect each other.

Ampère discovered that two parallel electrical currents moving in the same direction attract each other. Two parallel currents going in opposite directions repel, or push each other away. He also discovered that current going through a coil wound up like a spring acts like a magnet. This kind of coil is called a solenoid. Ampère's experiments showed that electrical currents have the same effect as magnets. He invented the astatic needle. The astatic needle made it possible to discover and measure electric current.

Ampère suggested that the earth's magnetism might be caused by electrical currents going around in the earth's center. The ampere, the unit of electrical current, was named after him. J.J.A./D.G.F.

André Ampère

AMPHETAMINE (am fet′ ə mēn′) Amphetamines are man-made drugs. One example is named Benzedrine. Amphetamines are also called speed. They are stimulants which can increase energy and mental alertness. Doctors prescribe them for treatment of mild depression, alcoholism, fatigue, and sleepiness. Because amphetamines increase metabolism, overweight people sometimes use them to help to lose weight. When too much is taken, amphetamines can cause restlessness, lack of sleep, irritability, nausea, and even death.

It is legal for doctors to prescribe amphetamines. However, they are often obtained illegally and used by people who do not need

them. Such use is dangerous because amphetamines can upset the metabolism of the body. They can also cause damage to the nervous system. People can become addicted to amphetamines. S.R.G./J.J.F.

AMPHIBIAN (am fib′ ē ən) An amphibian is a member of an ancient class of animals. The class came into existence about 350 million years ago. As a result of evolution, certain fish developed so they could breathe air and walk on land. The fins of some fish became legs. These fish evolved into amphibians. The name amphibian means ''double-life.'' Most amphibians lived part of their life in water and the rest on land. After about 50 million years, some amphibians evolved into reptiles. Reptiles are a group of similar animals which can live away from water. Although most amphibians disappeared, many have survived. Frogs, toads, and salamanders are amphibians.

Amphibians have backbones. Most of the adults have four legs. Even though all amphibians do not live in water, they do have to stay moist. The skin of humans prevents water from evaporating from their tissues. The skin of amphibians does not prevent evaporation. If the animal goes away from water on a hot day, it might dry up and die. Although most amphibians have lungs, they also breathe through their skin. Some salamanders breathe through gills, like fish. Amphibians lay eggs that must stay wet. Most amphibians lay eggs in water. Some of them, however, can lay their eggs in moist places such as under rotting logs and under leaves on the ground. The eggs that are laid in water hatch into tadpoles, or free-swimming larvae. Tadpoles live in the water and breathe through gills. When they change into adults, they can leave the water and breathe with lungs.

Amphibians are cold-blooded animals. This means that their body temperature does not remain at the same level at all times, but is the same temperature as their surroundings.

APODANS (CAECILIANS)

Among the most primitive of living amphibians, the apodans are mostly burrowing animals which live in the tropics. They are legless and have very small eyes, both of these features being adaptations to underground life. Their ancestors had thick armoured skin, and apodans still retain traces of this armour in the form of small dermal plates embedded in their skin.

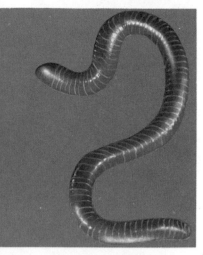

URODELES

The newts and salamanders are the least specialized of the amphibians. They have kept the general shape of their ancestors, the first land animals. But the pictures show that the newt tadpole and the frog tadpole are quite similar, even though the grown animals are very different. The resemblance of the larval stages is like the resemblance between embryos of certain mammals, such as the rabbit and man. The axolotl is really a giant tadpole, which can turn into a salamander. But some relatives of the axolotl stay always as tadpoles, giving birth to young tadpoles. This is an example of *neoteny*, an important process in the development of many animal types.

ANURANS

The frogs and toads are amphibians specialized for jumping. Toads usually have warty skins, and frogs smooth skins—otherwise there is little difference between them. Unlike other amphibians, anurans have voices, ranging from the high peeping of some tree-frogs to the deep croak of the bullfrog. Anurans are protected from their enemies by slimy skin substances. The skin slime of the Kokoi frog of South America is one of the most deadly poisons known.

All amphibians alive today belong to one of three groups: apodans, urodeles, and anurans. The apodans are legless, wormlike creatures found only in tropical regions. Some species live in the water, but most burrow in damp soil.

The urodeles are amphibians with tails. Salamanders and newts are urodeles. Many urodeles are completely terrestrial: they do not have to return to water. There are other salamanders which never leave the water, such as the mud puppy and the axolotl of North America. Some salamanders live in dark caves and do not have eyes. The largest amphibian is the giant salamander of Japan, which is 1.65 m [5.5 ft] long.

The anurans are the toads and frogs. They have hind legs which they use for jumping. Anurans vary in size from tiny tree frogs less than 2.5 cm [1 in] long to the goliath frog of tropical Africa, which reaches a length of about 1 m [3.3 ft] with its legs extended. Most anurans breed in the water and lay jellylike masses or strings of eggs. Frogs and toads eat insects, which they capture with their long, sticky tongues. Most frogs stay in or near water. Most toads, however, can travel away from water. S.R.G./C.J.C.

AMPLIFIER (am′ plə fī ′ər) An amplifier is a device that increases the strength or power of an electrical signal. It consists of vacuum tubes or transistors linked together in a circuit. Transistors have replaced vacuum tubes in many amplifiers. Vacuum tubes are still used whenever very high power is needed.

Amplification occurs in stages. Each tube or transistor strengthens the signal that passes through it. Microphones, radio antennas, and the pickups of record players produce weak signals. These are usually fluctuating voltages. They may be as little as one millionth of a volt. Amplifiers must be used to boost the power of these signals so they can be heard. Amplifiers are particularly important in public address systems. These systems are used when sound signals must reach many people in large rooms, or outdoors.

Amplifiers used to produce high quality sound in hi-fi systems are often expensive and complicated devices. *See also* ANTENNA; RADIO. W.R.P./L.L.R.

AMPLITUDE (am′ plə tüd′) Amplitude is the maximum distance a swinging or vibrating body moves from its place of rest, called its zero point. It is commonly used to measure the peak, or intensity, of sound waves and alternating electrical currents. A good example of amplitude is the movement of a simple pendulum, such as a weight attached to the end of a piece of string. If the weight is pulled aside and released, it will swing to and fro, or oscillate. The greatest distance the weight

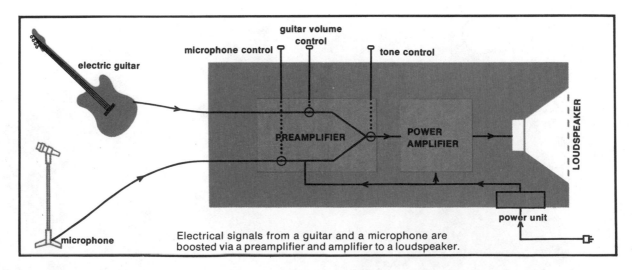

Electrical signals from a guitar and a microphone are boosted via a preamplifier and amplifier to a loudspeaker.

travels in either direction from its original resting point is its amplitude. The amplitude of a sound wave is the highest point of its pressure or velocity. Amplitude is the greatest change in voltage of an alternating electrical current from its average voltage. Amplitude may also refer to the height of ocean tides. *See also* SOUND.
W.R.P./L.L.R.

ANACONDA (an′ ə kän′ də) The anaconda is one of the largest snakes in the world. The anaconda is a member of the Boidae family. It is found in the northern countries of South America. It may grow as long as 9 m [30 ft] and as thick as a man's body. Unlike poisonous snakes, the anaconda does not kill its prey by biting. It wraps its body around its prey and squeezes the animal to death by suffocating it. Anacondas feed mostly on small mammals and birds. Sometimes they catch and swallow a caiman, which is a relative of the alligator. After the animal is dead, the anaconda swallows it whole. The anaconda spends much of its time in water.
S.R.G./C.J.C.

The huge anaconda never lives far from water. It spends much of its time swimming in rivers.

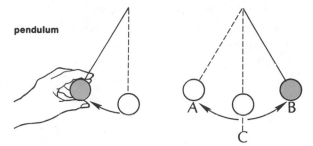

pendulum

Distance *AC* or *BC* is the amplitude of this pendulum.

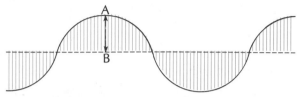

soundwave

Distance *AB* is the amplitude of this sound wave.

ANAEROBE (an′ ə rōb′) An anaerobe is an organism that lives and reproduces in an oxygen-free environment. Anaerobes do not carry out the process of respiration. (*See* RESPIRATION.) Many bacteria, fungi, and protozoans are anaerobic. They get their energy by breaking down either organic or inorganic compounds in a process called fermentation.

(*See* FERMENTATION.) Some yeasts, for example, convert sugar into alcohol by fermentation.

Obligate anaerobes are organisms that must live in a totally air-free environment. If they are exposed to the air, they will die. Facultative anaerobes can live either with or without air. They are able, therefore, to undergo either respiration or fermentation. *See also* AEROBE.   A.J.C./E.R.L.

ANALGESIC (an′ əl jē′ sik) An analgesic is a drug that reduces pain without causing unconsciousness or complete loss of feeling. Mild analgesics, such as aspirin, codeine, and paracetamol, are used to relieve headaches, rheumatism, and other body pains. More powerful analgesics include substances derived from opium. Two such analgesics are morphine and heroin. These are dangerous drugs which can cause addiction. They are used by doctors only for relieving intense pain of patients who are suffering from cancer or severe injuries. Many analgesics are also antipyretics, which reduce fever. *See also* ANESTHETIC.   S.R.G./J.J.F.

ANALOG COMPUTER   *See* COMPUTER.

ANATOMY

Anatomy (ə nat′ ə mē) is the study of how living things are built. The word anatomy comes from the Greek words that mean cutting up. Most of what is known about how an organism is put together was learned by someone who cut it apart, or dissected it, and looked at it. Today, scientists can study the inside of a living body with x-rays. Anatomy is very important in the education of a doctor.

There are many different types of anatomy. In gross anatomy, the naked eye is used to study large parts of a body. In microscopic anatomy, microscopes are used to study very small parts of a body. Comparative anatomy is the study and comparison of similar parts of the bodies in different species. A comparative anatomist may compare the hearts of a fish, frog, snake, and bird. Embryology is the study of embryos, which are developing, unborn babies. Histology is the study of the structure of tissues. Cytology is the study of the structure of cells. (*See* PHYSIOLOGY.)

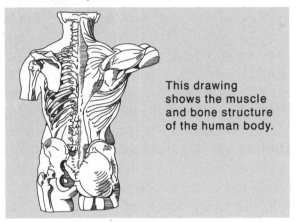

This drawing shows the muscle and bone structure of the human body.

Human anatomy   The study of the structure of the human body is called human anatomy. By understanding the parts of the human body and how they are built, doctors are able to heal injuries and cure diseases. All the parts of a body work together in a very complicated way to keep a person alive. Although doctors and scientists now know much about the human body, they still do not understand how every part works.

The body is made up of nearly 50 million million cells. These cells are grouped together in different types of tissues. There are skin tissue, muscle tissue, bone tissue, and other kinds of tissue. Tissues are grouped together and form organs, such as the brain, heart, and stomach. The organs work together in systems, to do certain jobs.

The skeletal system, or skeleton, is made up of all the bones in the body. There are 206 bones in the human body. They are connected in several ways. Joints, such as the knee, allow two connected bones to move. The muscular system is made up of all the muscles. They are attached to the bones. The muscles move the bones and allow a person to walk, swim, and move about.

The circulatory system is made up of the heart, arteries, veins, and blood. The blood carries food and oxygen to every cell in the body. It also carries waste products and carbon dioxide away from the cells. (*See* RESPIRATION.) The heart pumps the blood throughout the body. The blood leaves the heart through arteries and returns to the heart through veins. The lymphatic system acts in a similar way to remove other waste products from tissues.

The respiratory system provides oxygen from the air for the blood. This occurs in the lungs. When a person inhales, he is taking in oxygen for the blood to take to the cells. When a person exhales, he or she is removing carbon dioxide that the blood has removed from the cells.

The digestive system provides food for the blood to take to the cells. It brings food into the body through the mouth and throat. In the stomach and small intestine, food is changed into a form that the body can use. The blood carries the nutrients from the small intestine to the cells. The unnecessary parts of the food and body wastes are removed through the large intestine and anus. The kidneys, part of the excretory system, filter liquid waste from the blood and store it in the bladder. When the bladder is full, its contents are passed out of the body in the form of urine. The skin also gets rid of wastes by sweating.

The reproductive system allows the body to produce children. Gonads produce sex cells—eggs and sperm—which create an embryo when they combine. Each body has two gonads. A male gonad is called a testicle. A female gonad is called an ovary. The penis of the male transfers the sperm into the vagina of the female where the sperm and egg combine.

Two systems control all of the other systems to see that they work properly. The nervous system sends signals to parts of the body by impulses of the nerves. These impulses are similar to electricity. The system includes the brain, spinal cord, and nerves. The endocrine system sends signals to parts of the body by chemicals in the blood. These chemicals are called hormones. The endocrine system includes organs such as the pituitary gland, adrenal gland, and thyroid.

S.R.G./J.J.F.

ANCHOVY (an′ chō′ vē) An anchovy is a small, herringlike, marine fish belonging to the family Engraulidae. (*See* HERRING.) There are more than 100 species. Anchovies grow from 10 to 25 cm [4 to 10 in] in length. They have large eyes and mouths. Anchovies are found all over the world, and are especially abundant off the coasts of Peru and Chile. The fish is used to make animal meal, oil, and fertilizer. Species of the fish are filleted, salted, packed in oil, and sold as a food delicacy.

S.R.G./E.C.M.

ANDREWS, ROY CHAPMAN (1884–1960) Roy Chapman Andrews was an American naturalist and explorer. He was born in Beloit, Wisconsin. He was an authority on whales. In 1906 he joined the staff of the Museum of Natural History in New York City and became its director in 1935. Chapman led six paleontological expeditions to Tibet, China, Burma, Outer Mongolia, and the Gobi Desert during the 1920s. Among Chapman's most important discoveries were dinosaur eggs and the remains of the baluchitherium—a large land mammal that is thought to have lived more than 90 million years ago. His writings include *On the Trail of Ancient Man* (1926) and *Quest of the Snow Leopard* (1955).

ANDROID (an′ drŏid′) An android or automaton is a kind of machine that resembles a human being. It can be designed to imitate a limited repertory of human actions. Unlike a true robot, however, an android cannot be reprogrammed to perform the variety of tasks as a human is capable of performing.

The so-called androids in science-fiction stories are imaginary devices, some of which have the characteristics of robots, whereas others, made entirely of biologic materials, are meant to be indistinguishable from human beings. *See also* ROBOTICS.

ANDROMEDA (an dräm' əd ə) Andromeda is the name of a constellation in the northern sky. It contains the Andromeda Nebula (M31) which is really a spiral galaxy. The stars of Andromeda are about 2,200,000 light years away from earth. The Andromeda Nebula can be seen without a telescope. To the naked eye, it looks like a milky blur. Andromeda contains novae, or exploding stars. It also contains variable stars and star clusters. The constellation is named for a princess in Greek mythology. *See also* ASTRONOMY.

G.M.B./C.R.

ANEMIA (ə nē' mē ə) Anemia is a condition in which the amount of hemoglobin in a person's blood falls below normal. Hemoglobin is a protein containing iron. It is carried in the red blood cells of human blood and gives the

Andromeda Galaxy is the most distant celestial object that can be seen with the unaided eye. This galaxy is more than two million light years away. This means that the light we now see from Andromeda started its journey to earth when people were still living in caves. It is believed that this galaxy is like our own Milky Way. The two bright spots are smaller satellite galaxies of Andromeda.

blood its red color. Hemoglobin makes it possible for the blood to carry oxygen. (*See* BLOOD.) Symptoms of anemia are dizziness, shortness of breath, paleness of the skin, increased amounts of urine, and a poor appetite.

Disease, poor diet, allergy, and poison can all cause anemia. To cure anemia, doctors treat its cause. In many cases, people who are anemic are not eating foods with enough vitamins and iron in them. To cure the anemia, they must add vitamins to their diets. Women usually suffer from anemia more often than men do. *See also* MENSTRUAL CYCLE; SICKLE-CELL ANEMIA.   S.R.G./J.J.F.

ANEMOMETER (an′ ə mäm′ ət ər) An anemometer is an instrument that tells how fast the wind is blowing.

The simplest anemometer, known as the Robinson's anemometer, has three or four cups attached to a vertical pipe. The wind catches the cups, spinning them around. The wind's speed is measured by how many times the cups go around in a certain period of time. The hot wire anemometer is used to obtain a very accurate reading of wind speed. The pressure plate anemometer is often used in industries that must have exact recordings of wind speeds.

Airplane pilots and sailors need to know the speed of the wind. A meteorologist needs to use an anemometer when making a weather forecast. *See also* WEATHER.   J.J.A./C.R.

The cup anemometer is used to measure wind speed. When the wind blows against the cups, they rotate on their shaft. As the speed of the wind changes, so does the speed of rotation of the cups. A gauge on the shaft measures the number of rotations.

ANESTHETIC (an′ əs thet′ ik) An anesthetic is a substance that causes loss of feeling in the body. A local anesthetic causes the loss of feeling in a small part of the body, such as a finger. A general anesthetic causes loss of feeling throughout the entire body. Unconsciousness usually occurs when a general anesthetic is used.

Anesthetics are used by doctors to stop pain. When a cut has to be stitched closed, a doctor will inject a local anesthetic so that the patient will not feel the pain of the stitching. The patient remains awake and alert. When more extensive surgery is necessary, such as an operation to remove an appendix, a doctor will give the patient a general anesthetic. This will stop all pain and keep the patient asleep until the operation is over. A person called an anesthetist is trained to give the proper amount of anesthetic to patients. At least one anesthetist is always in the operating room during surgery.

Common anesthetics are nitrous oxide (''laughing gas''), chloroform, sodium pentothal (''truth serum''), and procaine. The use of anesthetics was first suggested by Sir Humphry Davy in 1799. They were first used, in 1844, by the American dentist Horace Wells.   S.R.G./J.J.F.

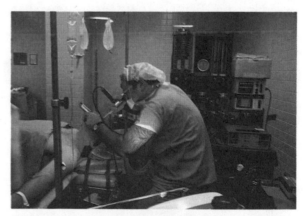

This picture of a modern operating room shows the use of an anesthetic machine during a surgical procedure.

ANGELFISH (an′ jel fish′) The angelfish is a freshwater fish belonging to the family Chaetodontidae. It lives in tropical regions where the water never gets very cold. It is also called scalare. There is another fish called the angelfish that lives in the ocean. The scalare has a very narrow, deep body with large fins. It is a very pretty fish and often kept in an aquarium.   S.R.G./E.C.M.

In nature, the angelfish lives near the surface. It is one of the most popular aquarium fish.

ANGIOSPERM (an′ jē ə spərm′) An angiosperm is a plant that grows flowers. All of its seeds are found inside a type of fruit. Not all of the flowers are bright and colorful like those found in gardens. For instance, even the grass in a lawn grows flowers. Grass flowers are small and green so they are rarely noticed. Grass also bears small fruit.

Angiosperms are the most common type of plant on Earth. There are more than 250,000 species. There are two groups of angiosperms: monocotyledons and dicotyledons. Monocotyledons have long, narrow leaves, flower parts in groups of three, and seeds with one leaf inside. Dicotyledons have wide leaves, flower parts in groups of four or five, and seeds with two leaves inside. *See also* PLANT KINGDOM.   S.R.G./M.H.S.

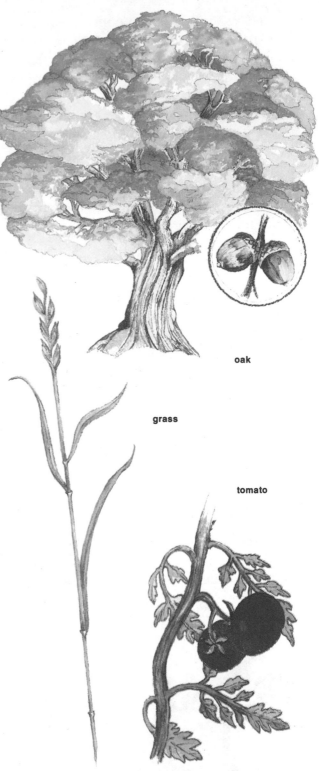

oak

grass

tomato

rose

Four well-known angiosperms. Three of these plants are not usually thought of as flowering plants, the descriptive term for angiosperms. Members of the grass family are valued for their seed rather than their flowers. And the tomato plant is significant because of the fruit it produces. Animals eat the nuts of the oak.

ANGSTROM UNIT (ang′ strəm yü′ nət) An angstrom unit is an extremely small unit of length. It is equal to one ten billionth of a meter. Its symbol is Å. Angstrom units are used to measure very short distances or lengths, like the size of atoms or the wave lengths of light rays. Yellow light, for example, has a wave length of about 6,000 Å. The angstrom unit was named for Anders Ångstrom, a Swedish physicist.

W.R.P./R.W.L.

ANHYDRIDE (an hī′ drīd′) Anhydrides are chemical compounds from which water has been removed. For example, taking water (H_2O) out of sulfuric acid (H_2SO_4) makes an anhydride. It is called sulfur trioxide (SO_3).

There are two kinds of anhydrides. An acid anhydride is what remains after water is taken out of an acid. A basic anhydride combines with water to form bases.

Anhydrides are important in chemistry. They are used in making other compounds. One of the most important anhydrides is acetic anhydride. It can be made into acetic acid.

J.J.A./A.D.

ANILINE (an′ əl ən) Aniline is a colorless, oily liquid with a pleasant smell. It is poisonous. Aniline is made by reducing nitrobenzene. The boiling point of aniline is 184.13°C [363.43°F]. Its freezing point is −6.3°C [20.7°F]. Aniline has the formula $C_6H_5NH_2$.

Aniline is used in the manufacture of rubber and drugs and in the making of dyes.

J.J.A./J.M.

ANIMAL KINGDOM

All animals are said to belong to the animal kingdom (an′ ə məl king′ dəm). Most animals can move. Most have eyes, legs, and a head. However, some simple animals do not have eyes, or legs, or a head. Some animals that live in the ocean look like plants. The sea anemone is an example of a plantlike animal. The easiest way to tell the difference between plants and animals is to see how they get their food. Plants make their own food by photosynthesis. Animals cannot use photosynthesis. They must get their food by eating plants or other animals. A tiny ameba and a huge whale have one thing in common. They must eat other living things.

There are over a million species of animals. Some live at the bottom of oceans. Some live at the top of mountains. Animals are found at the North Pole and at the equator. Some species only have one cell. Others have billions of cells. A sponge is a very simple animal that sits in one place. A human being is a very complex animal that can move around. Biologists try to divide the members of the animal kingdom into smaller groups. They study the characteristics of each animal. Then they decide to which group it belongs.

Each animal in the animal kingdom belongs to a smaller group called a phylum. (*See* CLASSIFICATION OF LIVING ORGANISMS.) The following are major phyla in the animal kingdom: Protozoa (one-celled, microscopic animals), Cnidaria (jellyfishes), Platyhelminthes (flatworms), Aschelminthes (roundworms), Mollusca (clams and octopi), Annelida (segmented worms), Arthropoda (insects, crabs, shrimp, spiders), Echinodermata (starfish), and Chordata (all higher animals with nerve cords). Most of the familiar animals have nerve cords and backbones. They are also called vertebrates. Fish, frogs, birds, dogs, cats, and humans are all vertebrates, members of Chordata. Animals that do not have backbones are called invertebrates.

The study of animals and the animal kingdom is called zoology. A scientist who studies zoology is called a zoologist. *See also* PLANT KINGDOM; PROTISTA.

S.R.G./R.J.B.

INVERTEBRATES

ANIMAL KINGDOM

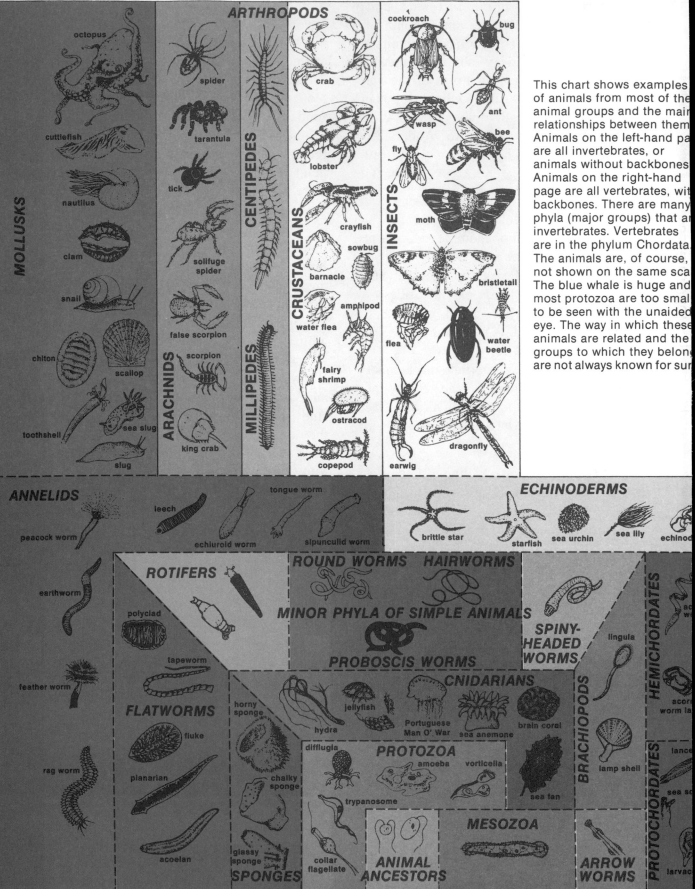

This chart shows examples of animals from most of the animal groups and the main relationships between them. Animals on the left-hand page are all invertebrates, or animals without backbones. Animals on the right-hand page are all vertebrates, with backbones. There are many phyla (major groups) that are invertebrates. Vertebrates are in the phylum Chordata. The animals are, of course, not shown on the same scale. The blue whale is huge and most protozoa are too small to be seen with the unaided eye. The way in which these animals are related and the groups to which they belong are not always known for sure.

VERTEBRATES

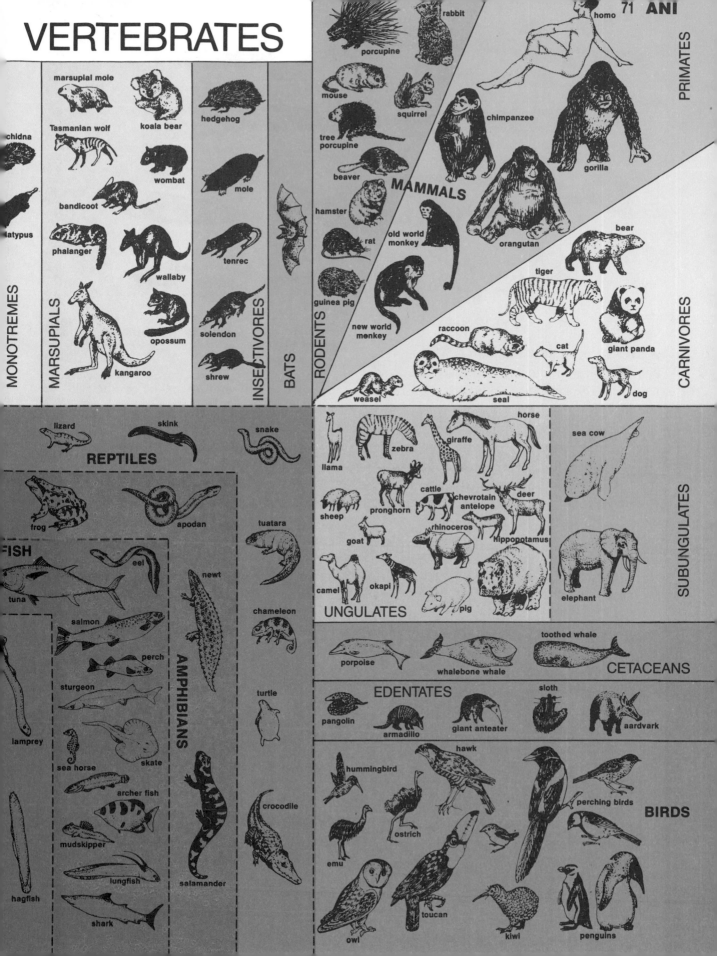

MONOTREMES

chidna

atypus

MARSUPIALS

marsupial mole

Tasmanian wolf

koala bear

bandicoot

wombat

phalanger

wallaby

kangaroo

opossum

INSECTIVORES

hedgehog

mole

tenrec

solendon

shrew

BATS

MAMMALS

RODENTS

porcupine

rabbit

mouse

squirrel

tree porcupine

beaver

hamster

rat

guinea pig

new world monkey

old world monkey

PRIMATES

homo

chimpanzee

gorilla

orangutan

CARNIVORES

bear

tiger

giant panda

raccoon

cat

weasel

seal

dog

REPTILES

lizard

skink

snake

FISH

tuna

eel

salmon

perch

sturgeon

lamprey

sea horse

skate

archer fish

mudskipper

lungfish

hagfish

shark

AMPHIBIANS

frog

apodan

newt

salamander

tuatara

chameleon

turtle

crocodile

UNGULATES

llama

zebra

giraffe

horse

sheep

pronghorn

cattle

chevrotain antelope

deer

goat

rhinoceros

hippopotamus

camel

okapi

pig

SUBUNGULATES

sea cow

elephant

CETACEANS

porpoise

whalebone whale

toothed whale

EDENTATES

pangolin

armadillo

giant anteater

sloth

aardvark

BIRDS

hummingbird

hawk

perching birds

ostrich

emu

owl

toucan

kiwi

penguins

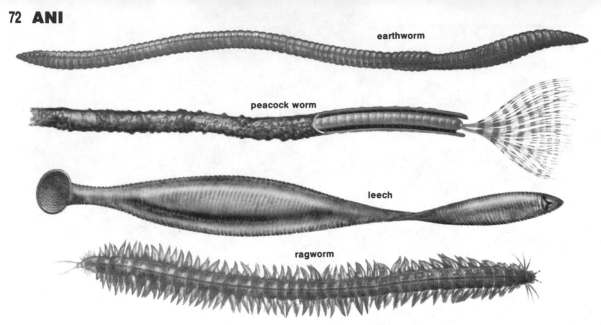

earthworm

peacock worm

leech

ragworm

Of the four typical annelids shown, the earthworm is perhaps the best known. The peacock worm and the ragworm are marine forms.

ANION (an′ ī′ ən) An anion is a negatively charged ion, or radical. It was discovered and named in 1834 by Michael Faraday, a British chemist.

Anions carry a specific number of negative electric charges. For example, the chlorine ion (Cl^-) has an electric charge of one, meaning it is a univalent anion. The sulfate ion ($SO_4 =$) has a negative electric charge of 2. It is a bivalent anion.

Anions move toward the positive electrode, or anode, during electrolysis. *See also* IONS AND IONIZATION. J.J.A./A.D.

ANNEAL (ə nēl′) Annealing is the manufacturing process by which molten metal or glass are gradually cooled. Controlled cooling of steel softens it and makes it more ductile, or easier to work with. Cooling is done first in a furnace, then in air. Glass is cooled slowly in annealing ovens to prevent strains and bubbles caused by carbon dioxide. Slow cooling allows heat to drive off the carbon dioxide.

Quenching and tempering are two other steel-making processes related to annealing. In quenching, the steel is heated to a critical temperature. It is then plunged into water or oil for quick cooling. This makes the steel strong, hard, and brittle. In tempering, steel is reheated to a temperature just below the critical temperature, and then cooled slowly. This softens the steel and increases its toughness. It also relieves strains. *See also* STEEL.

W.R.P./A.D.

ANNELIDA (a nel′ əd ə) Annelida is a phylum containing a large group of invertebrate animals. There are three classes of annelids: Polychaeta, marine worms; Oligochaeta, earthworms; and Hirudinea, leeches. Annelids, or segmented worms, are much more complex than Platyhelminthes (flatworms) and Aschelminthes (roundworms). Their patterns of development resemble those of arthropods and mollusks. *See* ANIMAL KINGDOM. S.R.G./C.S.H.

ANNUAL PLANT (an′ yə wəl plant) An annual plant is a plant that lives for only one growing season. It grows from a seed in the spring. It flowers in the summer. It scatters seeds and dies in the fall. The plants that appear the next spring grow from the seeds of the dead plant. Examples of annual plants are the sunflower and the sweet pea. *See also* PERENNIAL PLANT. S.R.G./M.H.S.

ANNUAL RING (an′ yə wəl ring) A circular line in the wood of a tree which shows how it has grown is called an annual ring. As a tree gets older, it grows taller and thicker. To grow thicker, a tree adds wood underneath its bark. In tropical regions where there is no winter, trees grow year-round. In places where there is a cold winter, trees stop growing during the winter.

When growth stops in the fall, the wood cells are smaller than they are in the spring, when growth continues. If a tree is cut down and sawn straight across, the change from fall to spring growth appears as a circular line in

This cross section of a tree tells the story of the tree's growth. Each ring represents a year of growth.

the wood. There is one ring in the wood for each year the tree has grown. The age of a tree can be told by counting the rings on its stump after the tree has been cut down.

Scientists learn about weather conditions in the past by studying the width of annual rings. The annual ring produced in a dry year is narrow. The annual ring produced in a wet year is wide. S.R.G./M.H.S.

ANODIZING (an′ ə dīz′ ing) Anodizing is a way of coating certain metals with an oxide film. This film resists corrosion. Aluminum and magnesium are the metals most often anodized. Sometimes, zinc is anodized.

The natural oxide film on aluminum is thin. Anodizing makes a thicker oxide layer. This protects the aluminum from corrosion and makes it last longer.

In anodizing, aluminum is used as the positively charged electrode of an electrolytic cell. Electrolytes like sulfuric acid are used. The oxide layer forms from the metal surface outward. This results in the outside layer being slightly rough and porous. It must be sealed by boiling it in water. This prevents harmful substances from attacking the metal.

Anodizing with sulfuric acid makes a clear oxide film. With chromic acid, a dull film is produced. The film may be dyed for decorative purposes. Chromic acid is also used for anodizing zinc. J.J.A./A.D.

ANT (ant) Ants are insects that belong to the order Hymenoptera. There are many thousands of species of ants. They are different sizes. Most ants, however, are smaller than an inch long. Ants are found in most parts of the world. They are related to bees.

Ants are social animals. This means that they live together in large colonies, or groups. Some colonies may contain millions of ants. Most colonies make nests in the ground or in dead trees. Others do not make nests. The army ants of the tropical jungles march to a different place every day. Thousands of them march in a narrow band and eat any animal that cannot get out of their way. Army ants can eat all the flesh off the bones of a dead animal very quickly.

There are different types of ants in each colony. Usually there is only one queen ant, a female that is the most important insect in the colony. The queen is the only ant that can lay eggs. When the eggs are fertilized by males, they hatch into female worker ants. When the eggs are not fertilized by males, they hatch into more male ants. (*See* PARTHE-

NOGENESIS.) Although there are thousands of worker ants in each colony, there are few male ants in a colony. Queen and male ants have wings. The queen and a male ant mate while flying in the air. Worker ants do not have wings. Worker ants collect food, feed the young ants, and build the nest. Some species of ants also have female soldier ants. They protect the nest.

Ants can do many things. They are able to travel long distances away from their nest and find their way back, because they follow their own chemical trails. Some ants can also grow food. They chew up leaves and store them in their nests. When a fungus grows on the leaves, they harvest the fungus for food. They also eat a sugary substance produced by aphids. Some species of ants keep aphids in almost the same way that humans keep milk cows. Ants are very strong. They can lift things much larger than themselves. They can lift things that weigh 50 times as much as they do. To match this, a person would have to lift nearly 9,091 kg [20,000 lb]. S.R.G./J.R.

ANTBIRD (ant′ bərd) Antbird is the general name for more than 225 kinds of birds living in the forests of Central and South America. They range in size from 7.5 to 37.5 cm (3 to 15 in) in length. Many feed on the forest floor, and have strong legs. Their beaks are usually hooked at the tip. Antbirds feed on ants, termites, beetles, moths, bees, spiders, and fruits. They are also called ant-wrens, ant-thrushes, and ant-shrikes. Antbird eggs are white with spots. The female lays two or so eggs in a nest often built in the fork of two or more branches. G.M.B./L.S.

ANTEATER (ant′ ēt′ ər) The anteater is a furry mammal. It belongs to the order Edentata, which means toothless. The anteater has a long, sticky tongue. Its snout is long and slender. With its powerful claws, it rips open the nests of insects. It eats ants and termites. Anteaters are nocturnal animals. They come

out mostly at night. The giant anteater is diurnal. It comes out mostly in the day. Anteaters live alone.

There are three kinds of anteaters: the giant anteater, the collared anteater, and the silky (or two-toed) anteater. The giant anteater is about 2.1 m [7 ft] long from the end of its tail to the tip of its nose. It wanders the forest floor in search of food. The collared anteater is about 1 m [3.3 ft] long. It gets its name from the coloration of fur around its shoulders, chest, and neck. The collared anteater climbs in trees and can hold onto branches with its tail. The silky anteater is 45.7 cm [18 in] long. It also climbs trees and uses its tail for holding. The silky anteater is sometimes called the two-toed anteater. *See also* AARDVARK; ARMADILLO; SLOTH.

G.M.B./J.J.M.

The tamandua is an anteater that lives in trees. It is about two ft [0.6 m] long.

ANTELOPE (ant′ əl ōp′) The antelope is a four-legged, hairy mammal that belongs to the family Bovidae. Antelopes are a type of ungulate, which is an animal with hooves. Antelopes are found in Africa and Asia, usually in large herds. They are all ruminants. This means they have four-part stomachs. All ruminants are cud-chewers. They swallow their food without having completely chewed it. Later this food is brought back up and re-chewed as cud. Then it is swallowed again.

Most antelopes are swift, delicate animals. They range in size, at shoulder height, from about 0.3 m [1 ft] to about 2 m [6 ft]. The smallest antelope is the royal antelope (*Neo-tragus pygmaeus*). The largest is the eland.

Both the male and female antelope may have horns. The horns on the female are usually smaller than those of the male.

Some of the best-known species of antelopes are the gnu, the blackbuck, and the impala. Antelopes provide a major food source for the large African and Asiatic carnivores. People also use the flesh of the antelope for food. The hide is often used for clothing, blankets, rugs, or ornamental purposes.

J.J.A./J.J.M.

ANTENNA (an ten′ ə) An antenna is a piece of equipment for sending and receiving electromagnetic radiation. It is a basic part of all electronic communication systems. It is used for radio, television, radar, and radio telescope operations. An antenna is also called an aerial.

There are two basic kinds of antennas. A dipole antenna has two pieces of metal or wire. A monopole antenna has a single metal or wire conductor that may be attached at one end to electrical ground. (*See* CIRCUIT.)

Antennas come in many shapes and sizes. Radio transmission antennas may be tall towers. Receiving antennas for transistor radios may be no bigger than a fingernail. Radar and radio telescope antennas often look like large metal dishes.

Some antennas, like those for television transmitters, must be put on the tallest buildings and the highest land peaks. A new kind of antenna for communications between a land base and underwater submarines can be placed underground.

The kind of antenna used depends on the type of electronic signal it sends or receives. Some signals require round, or loop, antennas. Other signals require vertical or horizontal antennas.

The design of an antenna must match the frequency or wavelength of its signal. AM radio antennas are used for low frequency signals. Low frequency signals have long wavelengths. Television antennas are used for high frequency signals. High frequency signals have short wavelengths. Radar and radio telescope antennas are used for very high frequency signals. Very high frequency signals have very short wavelengths called microwaves.

The first antenna was built by Heinrich Hertz, a German physicist, about 1887. His work with an antenna led to the invention of radio transmission and reception by Guglielmo Marconi, an Italian engineer, in 1896. *See also* ELECTRICITY.

G.M.B./L.L.R.

The two large antennas transmit signals from a network television station. The antennas are atop the John Hancock Center in Chicago, Illinois.

ANTENNAE (an ten′ ē) Antennae are sense organs of insects and other Arthropoda. The antennae project from the animals' heads and are used mainly for touching, smelling, or hearing. Tiny hairlike nerves in the antennae pick up sensations.

Ants use their antennae to follow a scent. The silk moth can use its antennae to smell another silk moth that may be many miles away. Insects that live in darkness often use their antennae to avoid bumping into things. Some small crustaceans use their antennae to move themselves through water. G.M.B./J.R.

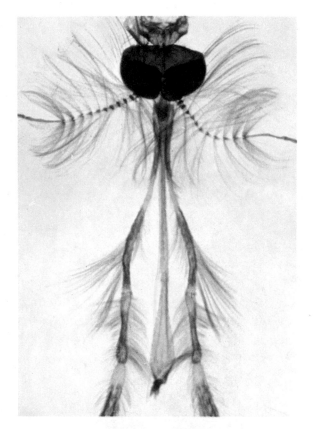

The antennae of insects are sense organs that project from the head. This picture of a mosquito shows antennae that are banded and feathery. The other head structures are mouth parts.

ANTHER (an′ thər) An anther is the male part of a flower. It contains the pollen, which is used in reproduction. The anther is connected to the flower by a filament. Anthers usually have two swollen parts, each of which contains two sacs. When the pollen is ripe, the swollen parts and the sacs break open. This releases the pollen. Some anthers open with a small explosion. The explosion blows the pollen into the air. Otherwise, the pollen stays on the anther. In either case, the wind may then blow the pollen away. Sometimes pollen from the anther sticks on the hairs of insects. They carry it away to other flowers. (*See* POLLINATION.) J.J.A./M.H.S.

ANTHERIDIUM (an′ thə rid′ ē əm) An antheridium is a male sex organ in a flower that makes sperm. It is found on ferns, mosses, and some species of algae and fungi. Antheridia are found on the upper surfaces of mosses and liverworts but are on the undersides of fern leaves. J.J.A./M.H.S.

The word anthropoid is used by zoologists to describe humans, apes, and monkeys, such as the baboon shown here. But in the term anthropoid apes, only the great apes—the gorilla, chimpanzee, gibbon, and orangutan—are included.

ANTHROPOID (an′ thrə poid′) An anthropoid is a highly developed mammal that is also a primate. Anthropoids form one of the two major groups of primates. Man, the apes, and the monkeys belong to this group. Other primates are included in the prosimian group.

An anthropoid has a flattened face with eyes in the front of the skull. Its brain is relatively large in proportion to its body. An anthropoid has stereoscopic vision, which allows it to judge depths of distance.

Scientists have identified several prehistoric primates as anthropoids. Among these are Neanderthal Man, Java Man, and *Australopithecus*. Scientists also believe that anthropoids evolved from prosimians. The prosimians are sometimes called lower primates. The anthropoids are sometimes called higher primates. *See also* EVOLUTION.

G.M.B./M.H.S.

ANTHROPOLOGY (an' thrə päl' ə jē) Anthropology is the study of mankind. It deals with the way humans lived in the past and the way humans live today. It began as a science in the 1800s. Anthropology is an outgrowth of biology and the social sciences. It has three main divisions: physical anthropology, cultural anthropology, and prehistory.

Physical anthropology deals with the development of the human body. It studies the skeletons of humans to learn how man has evolved and how man has changed. It also studies the differences between human beings who live in different places. The colors of hair and skin, the shapes of heads and bodies, and the different types of human blood are some of the things physical anthropologists study and compare.

Cultural anthropology deals with the way human beings live. Cultural anthropologists study ways in which people are different. They note such things as family and tribal structure. They study a society's customs, work habits, recreational pursuits, arts, crafts, music, and literature. They study the religion, agriculture, medicine, and tools of particular societies.

Louis Leakey of England and Margaret Mead of the United States are two famous anthropologists. Leakey, a physical anthropologist, devoted most of his time to searching for the skulls of prehistoric humans. He discovered, in Africa, the skulls of humans who lived millions of years ago. Margaret Mead, a cultural anthropologist, studied the life-styles of primitive people who lived without machines. She spent many years in the islands of the South Pacific studying primitive people. She also studied the aborigines of Australia, who still live the way they lived thousands of years ago. *See also*

ARCHEOLOGY; EVOLUTION; MAYAN CIVILIZATION. G.M.B./S.O.

ANTIBIOTICS

Antibiotics (an' tī bī ät' iks) Antibiotics are chemical substances produced by microorganisms to protect themselves against harm. Man often uses antibiotics to control diseases of plants and animals.

The first antibiotic discovered was penicillin. In 1928, Alexander Fleming, a British bacteriologist, found that a substance secreted by a mold called *Penicillium notatum* had stopped the growth of bacteria in a laboratory culture. He named the antibiotic after the mold, penicillin.

Scientists think that antibiotics work by interfering with the ability of other bacteria to acquire and absorb food. However, these bacteria soon begin to reproduce offspring that are not affected by the antibiotic. These new bacteria are said to be resistant to the antibiotic.

In 1957, the chemical structure of penicillin was discovered. By making changes in that structure, scientists were able to make new varieties of the antibiotic. Bacteria that had become resistant to the original drug could be controlled successfully with one of the new penicillin strains.

In the 1940s, Selman Waksman, an American biologist, tested soil bacteria and other organisms to find those that would produce antibiotics. As a result of his research, streptomycin, actinomycin, the tetracyclines, and other antibiotics were found. Streptomycin, the tetracyclines, and penicillin are called broad-spectrum antibiotics because they are used to treat many different kinds of infections. Some antibiotics are used only against particular diseases or germs. These are called narrow-spectrum antibiotics. Rifampicin, for

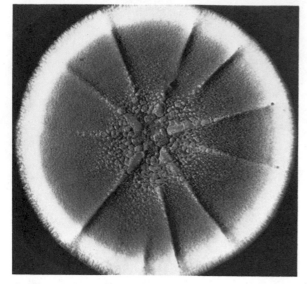

A colony of the mold *Penicillium*.

Disks impregnated with various antibiotics have been placed in a dish in which bacteria are being grown. Around the central disks, there is a wide ring in which the bacteria have not grown. This shows that the antibiotic in these disks strongly affected the bacteria.

example, is used only against certain virus infections such as smallpox. Actinomycin is used to prevent the growth of some cancers.

Antibiotics make up the most powerful group of drugs we have for controlling disease. They are used most successfully against diseases caused by bacteria and rickettsiae, many of which were once extremely dangerous to man. It is because of the use of antibiotics that serious infections and diseases such as tuberculosis, septicemia (blood poisoning), dysentery, syphilis, and typhus can be controlled.

Sometimes antibiotics are used to prevent infection. They are usually given to a patient before he has surgery in which a foreign object, such as a metal kneecap, is to be left in the body.

Some antibiotics are fed to healthy poultry and livestock to make them grow faster and to keep them healthy. Using antibiotics in the food of healthy animals means that many bacteria are allowed to build up a resistance to them. This means that the antibiotics will be less effective against disease and infection. Almost half the antibiotics produced in the United States are used in this way. In England, giving antibiotics to healthy animals is no longer legal.

This technician is making penicillin. The mold that produces this antibiotic is grown in a flask and then transferred to a stainless steel vessel, as shown here, under sterile conditions.

Thousands of antibiotics have been developed, but only 25 to 30 are in common use. Some are made out of chemicals.

Among the most recently developed antibiotics are amphoteicine b, nystatin, ampicillin, and cephalesporin. The first two are used to treat fungus infections. Ampicillin is used against intestinal infections, among others. Cephalesporin is an alternate antibiotic for people who are allergic to penicillin.

Some antibiotics prevent bacteria from multiplying. These are called bacteriostatic antibiotics. Chloramphenicol, erythromycin, and oleandomycin are three bacteriostatic antibiotics.   W.R.P./J.J.F.

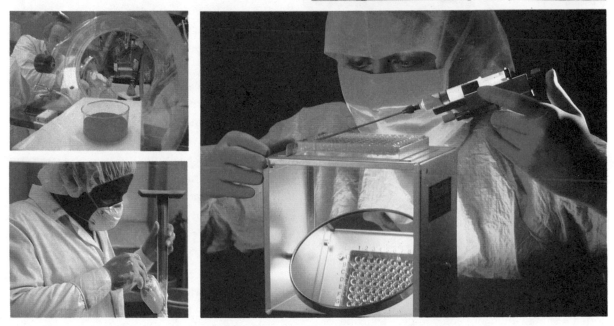

Some of the phases in the development and production of antibiotics include: design (above, left), analysis (above, right), diagnostics (below, right), sampling (below, bottom left), and observation (below, top left.)

ANTIBODY (ant' i bäd' ē) An antibody is a protein made by a living cell to fight infection. Antibody production is caused by the presence of antigens. Antigens are also proteins, but they do not belong in the body. These foreign substances are found in bacteria, viruses, insects, snake venom, and organs from another person. (*See* TRANSPLANTATION.) Both the antigens and the antibodies circulate in the blood plasma.

The body produces special antibodies to fight a certain antigen. The antibodies that destroy one antigen will not usually affect another one. Once the antigens causing an infection have been destroyed, the body may continue producing antibodies to fight that infection. If this happens, the body becomes immune to that infection. (*See* IMMUNITY.) An example of this is rubeola (common measles). Once a person recovers from

The picture shows the jutting contours of a small anticline, where rock layers are bent sharply upwards.

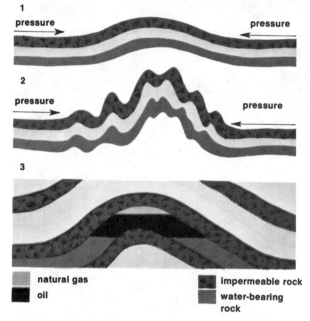

natural gas

oil

impermeable rock

water-bearing rock

Stages in the formation of an anticline: 1. pressure forms a simple anticline; 2. a complex anticline, or anticlinorium forms; 3. the crest of an anticline may be eroded away, with the anticline sometimes continuing underground. Oil and natural gas may be trapped at the crest of a water-bearing rock layer that is enclosed by two rock layers.

rubeola, the body continues making those antibodies, and he probably will not get the disease again. This is the principle behind vaccination. Weak antigens are injected into the body. The body starts producing antibodies which quickly destroy the antigens.

The body keeps making these antibodies, and the person does not get the disease. Vaccinations have controlled the spread of many diseases such as polio and measles.

Some antigens are poisons called toxins. Antibodies that neutralize these toxins are called antitoxins. Poisonous snakes have a strong toxin which they release through their fangs when they bite. The body starts to produce antitoxins to fight this poison. In some cases, the poison may be so strong that the body cannot produce enough antitoxins fast enough to fight it. Artificial antitoxins must be injected or the person will die. *See also* IN-TERFERON; LYMPHATIC SYSTEM. A.J.C./J.J.F.

ANTICLINE (ant′ i klīn′) An anticline is a bending in layers of rock that make up the earth's crust. It is also called an upfold, which is a formation that looks like an upside down U. An anticline is caused by sideways (horizontal) forces from opposite directions. These forces, or pressures, push the rock upward. (*See* STRATIFICATION.)

Some anticlines contain rock that is folded up and down. An anticline with upfolds and downfolds is called an anticlinorium. An anticlinorium has one major upfold. It also has minor upfolds and downfolds.

An anticline is most often identified by the crest, or the top of the fold. Geologists also identify anticlines by comparing rock on opposite sides of the crest. If the rock on both sides is the same, usually the geologic structure is an anticline.

Geologists used to think that anticlines were the most important sign of underground oil and gas. In the 1930s, geologists began to realize that anticlines are not the only important signs of such deposits of energy resources. *See also* FOLDING; GEOLOGY; PETROLOGY.   G.M.B./W.R.S.

ANTICYCLONE (ant' i sī' klōn') An anticyclone, or high, is a large moving area of high barometric pressure that is marked by clear skies and low humidity. Wind circulates in a clockwise direction around a high pressure center in the northern hemisphere. In the southern hemisphere, it circulates in a counterclockwise direction.

An anticyclone is the opposite of a cyclone, or low. A cyclone is a large moving area of air that is marked by low barometric pressure, cloudy skies, and precipitation.

Anticyclones move from west to east across the United States. They travel slowly and can remain stationary for several days. Cumulus, or fair-weather clouds, can form in an anticyclone. (*See* CLOUD.) Smog can occur over densely populated areas when winds are too light to blow away exhaust smoke from cars and factories.

Summer anticyclones in temperate regions feature warm temperatures, clear skies, and light winds. Winter anticyclones have low temperatures, clear skies, and strong winds. A Bermuda high is an anticyclone that affects the eastern part of the United States several times each summer. It is a stationary high, centered near Bermuda, an island off the coast of North Carolina. The Bermuda high brings warm, humid air from the Caribbean area into the southeastern and eastern states.

Permanent anticyclones can form over land and ocean areas. Much of Siberia is covered by a large anticyclone every winter. The horse latitudes of the oceans, 30°N and 30°S, have permanent anticyclones. They create trade winds, steady breezes that blow in one direction for weeks at a time. When sailing ships were common, they used these winds to cross the oceans. *See also* WEATHER.

W.R.P./C.R.

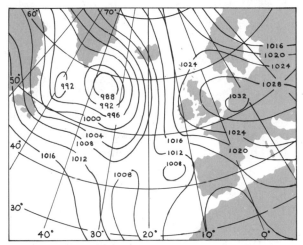

A weather map showing an anticyclone over Europe and a cyclone over the north Atlantic Ocean. The numbers indicate millibars of air pressure. Pressures are lowest in the center of a cyclone and highest in the center of an anticyclone, as shown on this map.

ANTIDOTE *See* POISON.

ANTIFREEZE (ant' i frēz') An antifreeze is a substance that, when added to a liquid, lowers the freezing point of that liquid. The main ingredient of an antifreeze is usually a type of alcohol.

Ethylene glycol is the basis of the most common antifreeze. It is used in the cooling systems of internal combustion engines, such as those in many automobile engines. During the cold winter months, this antifreeze is used alone or with water to prevent the freezing of the cooling system. Methanol is sometimes used as an antifreeze in internal combustion engines. Methanol lowers the freezing point of water. These antifreezes are often drained out of the cooling system after the threat of freezing is over. Often, because of evaporation, antifreeze loses its power, no longer protecting the cooling system from rust and corrosion. It can also creep into the block of an engine and cause problems in lubrication.

Ethylene glycol is also used to prevent icing of propellers and wings of airplanes. Glycerol and ethyl alcohol are used to protect drugs and cosmetics from freezing during storage. Calcium chloride and sodium chloride, unlike other antifreezes, are salts used in refrigeration. J.J.A./J.M.

ANTIMATTER (ant′ i mat′ ər) All matter is made up of very small particles called elementary particles. Protons, neutrons, and electrons are all elementary particles. All elementary particles have a corresponding antiparticle. These antiparticles are almost identical to their ordinary particles. They have the same mass but some other properties, such as electric charge, are reversed. For example, an electron has a negative charge. Its antiparticle is called a positron and it has a positive charge. A proton has a positive charge. Its antiparticle, called an antiproton, has a negative charge. Antiparticles are produced in nuclear reactions made by particle accelerators.

Particles and their antiparticles destroy each other when they come in contact. Radiation, in the form of gamma rays or X-rays, is produced in the reaction. Antiparticles produced in particle accelerators have very short lives. This is because all matter on earth is made of ordinary particles. An antiparticle quickly collides with an ordinary particle and is destroyed.

All matter is made of atoms. Atoms themselves are made of protons, neutrons, and electrons. Antimatter would have atoms made out of antiprotons, antineutrons, and positrons. Scientists believe that antimatter may exist in the universe. Quasars give off huge amounts of energy. This may be caused by the coming together of matter and antimatter.

The big bang theory suggests that the universe was created by a single, large explosion. This explosion could have produced matter and antimatter in equal amounts. The high temperature of such an explosion could have kept the two apart. Then they could have moved to various parts of the universe. There are huge amounts of radiation in the universe. This could be caused by this matter and antimatter coming together. But nobody knows if this is true or not. M.E./J.T.

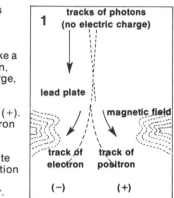

Antimatter actually has been observed in experiments. Photons—packets of light—are made to strike a lead plate. Each photon, having no electric charge, then breaks into an electron (−) and its antiparticle, a positron (+). The electron and positron are separated by a magnetic field, which attracts them in opposite directions. This separation keeps them from annihilating each other.

ANTIMONY (ant′ ə mō′ nē) Antimony is a brittle, white metallic element. Its symbol is Sb.

Antimony is extracted from a gray sulfide mineral called stibnite. The stibnite is heated with scrap iron in a furnace. The iron combines with sulfur in the stibnite and forms iron sulfide. This frees the antimony. Because it is heavier than iron sulfide, its sinks to the bottom of the furnace. It is then drawn off.

Pure antimony has few uses. It can be combined with other metals to form alloys. (*See* ALLOY.) These alloys have many uses. Antimony expands as it cools. For this reason it is used in alloys for casting molds. It forms strong, hard alloys with tin, lead, and copper. These alloys are used in bullets, machine bearings, and automobile storage batteries. Compounds of antimony have many uses. They are used in matches, plastics, paints, and some medicines. M.E./J.R.W.

ANTISEPTIC (ant′ ə sep′ tik) An antiseptic is a chemical that either kills or stops the growth of bacteria. It is not as strong as a germicide, which completely destroys the bacteria. (*See* DISINFECTANT.) Antiseptics are used in operating rooms of hospitals to make sure no bacteria can enter the patients' bodies and cause infection. First-aid medicine includes antiseptics to stop any bacteria that may be present around a cut. *See also* ASEPSIS.

S.R.G./J.J.F.

ANTITOXIN (ant′ i täk′ sən) An antitoxin is a chemical made by organisms to protect themselves against toxins. A toxin is a poisonous chemical produced by an organism. The human body produces many antitoxins to fight toxins that are produced by disease-causing bacteria. The bacteria that cause diphtheria and tetanus produce toxins that can kill a human. When a person does not have any antitoxin in his blood, a doctor will inject some from another animal to help the person fight the toxins. *See also* ANTIBODY; IMMUNITY; INFECTION.

S.R.G./J.J.F.

ANTLER (ant′ lər) Antlers are bone growths from the heads of most male deer and some female deer. The only male deer without antlers are the Chinese water deer and the musk deer. The caribou and reindeer are the only kinds of deer in which both the males and females have antlers. Antlers are used for defense. They are also used during the mating season when male deer fight head-on for female mates.

Unlike the horns of other animals, deer antlers are solid bone. Horns are hollow, bony growths with a skinlike covering. Antlers are part of the skeleton. Horns are not part of the skeleton.

Deer lose their antlers every spring after mating season. New antlers grow during the summer, fall, and winter months. At first, the new antlers are covered with a velvety tissue. When the antlers are fully developed, this

Antlers grown by deer provide ornamentation and weaponry. In some species both females and males grow antlers, but in most species of deer only the males grow them. New antlers grow each year, starting in early summer. They are shed in the first few months of the year.

covering dries and cracks. Deer rub their antlers against trees to rid their antlers of this dead tissue.

The moose is the largest member of the deer family. Its antlers sometimes grow to 1.8 m [6 ft] in width. Other deer antlers range from short and spiky to long and branched.

In prehistoric times, humans made tools out of antlers. In China, antlers are still used in the making of some medicines. Hunters often mount the antlers of deer they have killed as trophies to hang on walls.

The size of antlers is usually determined by the age of a deer. When some deer get very old, their antlers become smaller. A deer's health and the environment it lives in also determine the size and condition of its antlers.

G.M.B./R.J.B.

ANT LION (ant lī′ ən) The ant lion family, Myrmeleontidae, includes hundreds of species of insects that trap ants and other small insects for food. An ant lion is actually the larva of an insect which looks like a dragonfly. An ant lion has a fat, bristly body and two long, sickle-shaped jaws.

An ant lion captures its prey in a small, sandy, funnel-shaped pit which is rarely more than 5 cm [2 in] across and 2.5 cm [1 in] deep. An ant lion forms this trap by turning around and around while throwing sand or earth with its jaws and head. The ant lion eventually buries itself in the bottom with just its jaws sticking out of the sand. When an ant or other small insect walks near the edge of the pit, the sand gives way and the insect slides toward the ant lion's powerful jaws. These jaws are stuck into the prey and its body juices are sucked out.

An adult ant lion does not eat. It lives for a few months until the food it stored during its larval stage is used up. The entire life cycle of an ant lion takes less than 12 months. (*See* METAMORPHOSIS.) The ant lion is most common in tropical areas. *See also* LACEWINGS.

A.J.C./J.R.

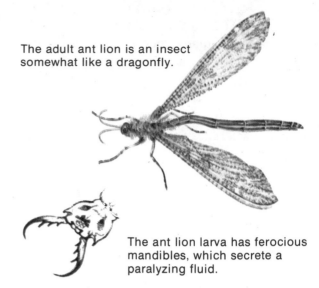

The adult ant lion is an insect somewhat like a dragonfly.

The ant lion larva has ferocious mandibles, which secrete a paralyzing fluid.

ANUS (ā′ nəs) The anus is the opening at the lower end of the alimentary canal. All organisms with a complete digestive system have a mouth through which food can be taken and an anus through which wastes pass from the body. Anal sphincter muscles surround the anus of most animals. These muscles control the release of feces by controlling the opening and closing of the anus. Feces are wastes left over from digestion. A baby does not have control over the anal sphincter muscles. Control of them is voluntary and must be learned. (*See* MUSCLE.) *See also* DIGESTION; INTESTINES.

A.J.C./J.J.F.

AORTA (ā ȯrt′ ə) The aorta is the largest and longest artery in the human body. It carries oxygen-rich blood away from the heart to the other major arteries. The aorta starts in the left ventricle and rises to near the bottom of the neck. It then arches backward and downward through the chest and abdomen. Arteries branch off the aorta along its entire length. These arteries supply blood to the heart muscle, the brain, and all internal organs. muscles, and bones. *See also* CIRCULATORY SYSTEM.

A.J.C./J.J.F.

APATITE (ap′ ə tīt′) Apatite is a common mineral which is a calcium phosphate. Apatite also contains chlorine or fluorine. Its name comes from the Greek word *apate*, meaning "deception." The mineral is well named, as apatite may look like several other minerals. Its crystals may be brown, yellow, green, blue, violet, white, or even colorless. Apatite is found in many kinds of rocks. In North America, Florida is the main source of apatite. Other large deposits are found in the Soviet Union and North Africa.

Apatite has the hardness standard 5 in Mohs scale. Its relative density is about 3.2. Apatite is used in the making of fertilizer and phosphoric acid.   J.J.A./R.H.

APE (āp) Apes are primates belonging to the family Pongidae. Apes have long arms, fingers, and toes. They have hairy bodies with no tails. Apes have large brains and are probably second in intelligence only to human beings. Apes live in tropical areas of Asia and Africa. The great apes include chimpanzees, gorillas, and orangutans. The smaller, lesser apes include the six kinds of gibbons. Monkeys are different from apes because monkeys have tails and do not walk upright.

Apes look similar to human beings. Apes, though, do not stand completely upright. When they walk, they use their arms and knuckles to help support their weight.
                                    A.J.C./J.J.M.

APHID (ā′ fəd) An aphid, or plant louse, is a small, soft-bodied insect that damages plants. The aphid has a needle-shaped mouth that it sticks into a plant. It then sucks out the plant juices. Aphids can often spread disease from one plant to another. Aphids may be any of several colors, but most are green or black. The male usually has four wings. The female is often wingless.

After mating in the fall, the female lays her eggs. These eggs hatch in the spring. The newborn aphids, which are females, then give birth to other living aphids from unfertilized eggs within their own bodies. This par-

thenogenesis produces many aphids each summer.

Some kinds of aphids have a symbiotic relationship with ants. (*See* SYMBIOSIS.) The aphids produce a sweet, waxy fluid called honeydew. Ants protect the aphids in exchange for this honeydew. *See also* BUG.
                                    A.J.C./J.R.

This greenfly is a destructive aphid, or plant louse.

APOLLO PROJECT *See* PROJECT APOLLO.

APOPLEXY (ap′ ə plek′ sē) Apoplexy is a condition that results when the brain does not receive the proper amount of blood. This can result in brain damage and death. Apoplexy is also called a stroke.

Apoplexy may be caused by a blood clot in the brain or in an artery leading to the brain. It may also come as a result of arteriosclerosis. Sometimes it is caused by a break in a blood vessel in the brain. When one of these things occurs, part of the brain does not get blood and is injured. Since the brain controls the entire body, the regions of the body controlled by the injured part of the brain will be affected. Victims of apoplexy may suffer paralysis. They may be unable to walk or talk.

Apoplexy may be treated by removing the blood clots through surgery, by the use of medicine, or by the surgical repair of broken blood vessels. *See also* CIRCULATORY SYSTEM.   S.R.G./J.J.F.

APPENDIX (ə pen′ diks) The appendix is a part of the intestines in humans. Its full name is the vermiform appendix. The appendix is found on the lower right side of the abdomen. It is about 2.5 cm to 15.25 cm [1 to 6 in] in length. The appendix is attached to the caecum. The caecum is a part of the intestines found between the large and small intestines.

Although the appendix does not serve a useful purpose today, it was probably a necessary part of the digestive system thousands of years ago. A person's diet was different then from what it is now. *See also* DIGESTION.

S.A.B./J.J.F.

APPLE

blossom

fruit

The apple tree is an important member of the rose family.

APPLE (ap′ əl) An apple is the fruit of about 25 species of trees belonging to the family Rosaceae. There are thousands of kinds of apples in three categories: cooking apples, cider apples, and dessert apples. When ripe, apples are usually red, yellow or green. They have round shapes and measure 5 to 10 cm [2 to 4 in] in diameter.

Apples grow in most parts of the United States and in both hemispheres. Apple trees require long dormancy, which means that some period of relatively cold weather is needed. Apples cannot usually be grown in most tropical places.

Scientists believe the apple originated thousands of years ago in Turkey as the fruit of a wild roselike shrub. Since then, humans have developed that wild plant into the many kinds of apple trees we know today.

Apples contain vitamins A and C. They are sources of cellulose and are high in carbohydrates. G.M.B./F.W.S.

APRICOT (ap′ rə kät′) An apricot is the fruit of a tree belonging to the family Rosaceae. It has a smooth pit called a stone at its center. It looks like a yellow peach except that its skin is not fuzzy like that of a peach. Apricot trees grow best in fairly warm places. These trees resist drought well. They can live as long as 100 years.

An apricot can be eaten fresh as a dessert fruit. It also can be preserved by canning and drying. Apricots are a good source of vitamin A. They also are high in natural sugar content. Dried apricots are an excellent source of iron.

Scientists believe the apricot tree originated in China thousands of years ago. Today, it grows throughout the earth's temperate zones. Spain is the world's leading producer of apricots. Most of the apricots grown in the United States come from California.

G.M.B./F.W.S.

AQUARIUM (ə kwar′ ē əm) An aquarium is a container of water in which aquatic plants and animals are kept. Most aquaria are glass so that one may see into them. Fish are often kept in home aquaria for enjoyment. Many scientific laboratories have aquaria so that organisms can be studied without the necessity of traveling to a lake or ocean to do so. An aquarium must be supplied with the proper light, heat, air, and food so that the plants and animals can live much as they do in nature.

Another type of aquarium is a large building where fish, reptiles, other animals, and plants are displayed for the public to see. Two well-known aquaria are the New England Aquarium in Boston and the John Shedd Aquarium in Chicago. S.R.G./E.R.L.